Practical Exercises
in APPLIED
STATISTICS

JULIE CHARLTON *and* **ROGER WILLIAMSON**

OXFORD UNIVERSITY PRESS

Oxford University Press, Great Clarendon Street, Oxford OX2 6DP

Oxford   New York

Athens   Auckland   Bangkok   Bogota   Bombay

Buenos Aires   Calcutta   Cape Town   Dar es Salaam

Delhi   Florence   Hong Kong   Istanbul   Karachi

Kuala Lumpur   Madras   Madrid   Melbourne

Mexico City   Nairobi   Paris   Singapore

Taipei   Tokyo   Toronto

and associated companies in

Berlin   Ibadan

Oxford is a trade mark of Oxford University Press

© Oxford University Press

First published 1996

ISBN 0 19 914310 2

A CIP catalogue record for this book is available from the British Library.

Typeset and illustrated by Gecko Ltd, Bicester, Oxon

Printed in Great Britain by Scotprint Ltd, Musselburgh

Contents

Introduction

'Distortions. Interference. Real data is messy.'

from *Arcadia*, Tom Stoppard

It is widely accepted that practical work is an essential part of learning Statistics. There are problems associated with incorporating such work into daily classroom teaching. With an uncertain understanding of a new topic, students often find it difficult to design and carry out a piece of practical work with any measure of success. Data collection often becomes very time-consuming and, having collected the data, students are unclear how to analyse it and report the various aspects of their investigation. This book offers a collection of short, highly structured statistical exercises with clear instructions on how to collect and analyse data and the points that should be addressed in the report. Each exercise is designed to illustrate a particular statistical technique or concept. The exercises are suitable for students of Statistics at AS-Level or A-level and first year university level or the equivalent. Most, with extension, could be presented as projects for submission as part of course assessment. These exercises have been trialled with A-level students.

Each chapter contains exercises on a particular topic, with each exercise emphasising a particular aspect of that topic. Also each chapter begins with notes for students. These are not intended to replace a textbook but give basic formulae and deal with points which students often find difficult.

Chapter 14 consists of five student reports on a selection of exercises. These are included exactly as they were written by the students and are not intended to be model answers. They are presented with teacher comments in order to show students what makes a good report: the organisation and depth of response expected, how to use appendices, and some idea of a suitable report length.

The selection of Notes on Exercises (Chapter 15) elaborates on the teaching points each exercise is designed to illustrate. However, as the students collect their own data, the intended outcome cannot be guaranteed. These notes are felt to be necessary for a student working alone but teachers may prefer to encourage students to complete an exercise before reading the corresponding notes.

Structure of the exercises

Requirements:

List of all equipment needed

Data Collection:

Details of pilot study (if appropriate), method of data collection, suggested size of sample/number of subjects.

Analysis:

List of tables, diagrams and calculations to be performed.

Conclusions:

Statements/questions to be considered in the conclusions section of the report.

These should be regarded as a stimulus to discussion rather than a list to be 'answered'.

Extensions:

Some (not necessarily comprehensive) suggestions for further work on this topic/set of data, to lead students towards converting the exercise into a substantial project.

Statistical projects

Many A-level and other Statistics courses require students to carry out a project. The project should have a purpose and the statistical techniques used should be chosen because they are the best available means of achieving the purpose. (This contrasts with the exercises in this book whose purpose is to illustrate a particular statistical technique.) The choice of project topic is extremely important and must be considered in the light of the relevant syllabus. A project which takes a set of data and applies all of the techniques in the syllabus to it, regardless of their relevance, is a poor project. However, one which uses only relevant statistical techniques may be equally unsatisfactory if the only relevant techniques are trivial or come from only one small corner of the syllabus.

The ideal project uses a wide spread of relevant techniques from the syllabus. It has a coherent overall plan and demonstrates skills of data collection, presentation, statistical analysis and inference. Of course, not all of these areas can be present in equal measure in each project.

Carrying out exercises from this book will help students with their projects in a number of ways:

(i) Practice will make them more adept at data collection.

(ii) The questions asked in the conclusions section will give them guidelines about the areas to cover in the project conclusions.

(iii) Experience of carrying out exercises will help them to see whether or not a project idea will be practical in the light of the available statistical techniques.

(iv) The extensions will suggest ways in which an exercise may be expanded into a project.

The main area where additional effort will be needed in a project is in data collection. In the exercises (apart from those specifically concerned with sampling) students have been encouraged to use whatever data is readily to hand and to comment on any biases this may have introduced. In a project, rather more effort to avoid bias in data collection is required. However, even in a project, a perfect solution is rarely available and the most important thing is to demonstrate that the problems of sampling have been considered and that reasonable efforts have been made to overcome them.

Acknowledgements

Extracts from BS 6001: Part 1: 1991 on p. 105 are reproduced with the permission of BSI. Complete editions of the standards can be obtained by post from BSI Customer Services, 389 Chiswick High Road, London W4 4AL.

Tables 3a–3f on p. 136 are reproduced with the permission of the Department of Trade and Industry.

The extract from *Arcadia* by Tom Stoppard on p. v is reproduced with the permission of Faber and Faber.

The authors also wish to thank the following pupils who acted as guinea pigs in the development of these exercises. Their comments on both the wording and feasibility of the exercises were most helpful and have been incorporated into the final version – Caroline, Sona, Gemma, Alison, Chew Ling, Claire, Deborah, Jane, Amy, Comino and Joanna.

1 Sampling

Notes for students

A **population** is the set of all possible data under investigation. For example, a statistician may want to investigate the income of adult British females. The population is the set of incomes of all adult British females – it is the *incomes*, not the individuals. If care is taken with the definition of 'adult', 'British', 'income' and 'female', it is theoretically possible to list this population. In practice, it cannot be done.

Some populations are infinitely large and so cannot be listed. For example, there is no limit to the number of times a die can be thrown, so it is impossible to list the population of outcomes. (Do not confuse the population with the sample space, which is a list of all of the *different* possible outcomes – 1, 2, 3, 4, 5, 6.)

A **sample** is a subset of the population. A sample is used when it is impossible, unnecessary or impractical to collect all of the population data.

A **statistic**, such as the mean, standard deviation or proportion, is calculated from a sample. The statistic is used to estimate a **parameter**, the equivalent property of the population from which the sample is drawn.

Types of sample

1. **Subjective** or **convenience:** The sample is chosen by the surveyor.
   Advantages Easy.
   Disadvantages May have hidden biases. Statistical calculations, such as confidence intervals, are not valid because the sample is not random.

2. **Random:** All members of the population have an equal chance of being included, as do all subsets of the appropriate size.
   Two types: Simple – without replacement
   Unrestricted – with replacement
   Advantages Unbiased estimates of population parameters and confidence intervals may be obtained. Hypothesis tests may be carried out.
   Disadvantages May be difficult or impossible to obtain. Requires a list of the population.

3. **Systematic:** Every nth item is chosen from a list of the population until a sample of the required size is obtained.
   Advantages Quick and easy. Unbiased if the population is arranged randomly with respect to the characteristic under investigation.
   Disadvantages May contain unsuspected biases. Requires a list of the population.

4. **Stratified random:** Prior knowledge is used to divide the population into homogeneous (with respect to the characteristic under investigation), mutually exclusive strata. A random sample is taken from each stratum.
   Advantages Is likely to give a more representative subset of the population than simple random sampling.
   Disadvantages Needs accurate prior knowledge and a list of the population.

5. **Quota** or **subjective stratified:** As stratified random sampling, but samples are chosen for convenience.
   Advantages Quick. When skilfully designed and executed yields good results.
   Disadvantages Easily abused. Statistical calculations such as confidence intervals are not valid because the sample is not random.

6. **Cluster:** Used when the population falls naturally into groups which facilitate the collection of the samples. Samples are selected at random from each cluster.
   Advantages Easy.
   Disadvantages Statistical calculations such as confidence intervals are not valid because the sample is not random. The clusters may not all be representative of the population.

The basic tool of statistical theory is a **random sample**. Stratified random sampling is an improvement on this. The alternative sample types are not as good but can be used when it is impracticable to obtain a random sample.

1.1 Library books

Students may wish to work together on this exercise in order to save time calculating the population mean and standard deviation. The sampling should be done individually and the results pooled so that there is a minimum of 10 samples of each size.

Requirements:
- a shelf in a library containing about 100 library books. The exercise works best when books have been borrowed frequently (do not choose a shelf from the reference section)
- random numbers from a table or a calculator

Data collection:
- record, for each book, the number of times, x, that it has been stamped (borrowed from the library) during the last 12 months. This is the population
- using random numbers each student should take a simple random sample (that is, without replacement) of size 5 and record, for each book, the number of times, y, that the book has been stamped
- using random numbers each student should take a simple random sample (that is, without replacement) of size 20 and record, for each book, the number of times, z, that the book has been stamped

Analysis:
- calculate the mean, μ, and the standard deviation, σ, of the population
- calculate the mean, $\bar{y}_i$, of each random sample of size 5
- calculate the mean, $\bar{z}_i$, of each random sample of size 20
- draw a dot plot of $\bar{y}_i$. Mark μ on the diagram
- draw a dot plot of $\bar{z}_i$. Mark μ on the diagram

Conclusions:
- are the $\bar{y}$'s good estimators of μ?
- is there evidence of bias?
- are the $\bar{z}$'s good estimators of μ?
- is there evidence of bias?
- compare the distribution of $\bar{y}$ with the distribution of $\bar{z}$
- the population is now defined as all of the books owned by the library. The books on your shelf are a sample used to estimate the average number of times a book has been borrowed in the last 12 months.
  What biases will have been introduced by:
  (i) taking all of the books from the same shelf?
  (ii) the fact that some books are less than 12 months old?
  (iii) the fact that some books are out on loan and therefore are not on the shelf?

Extensions:
- take systematic samples and/or subjective samples from the shelf and compare the means with μ
- if information about the average number of times a book is borrowed is available from the library, stratify the books by category (fiction, biography, etc.). Take a stratified random sample and/or a quota sample and use the means to estimate this average. Attempt to overcome the biases mentioned in the last part of the conclusions
- use samples to estimate σ

1.2 Christmas club

A large number of samples is required and so this exercise is best done by a class rather than by an individual student. Students may wish to work together to calculate the population mean and standard deviation.

Christmas Clubs are savings schemes run by shops. The diagrams on pages 5–14 represent, in bar form, the amount of savings per Christmas Club member in the 10 branches of a small chain of shops.

Requirements:
- random numbers from tables or a calculator

Section A

Data collection:
- each student should take the following 3 samples (alternatively, a single student can take at least 5, preferably more, of each type of sample)

    1. **Subjective sampling:** choose a sample of size 10 from the population of 480 accounts which you think will give a good estimate of the mean savings (do not use random numbers for this sample)
       Collect a second subjective sample of size 40. This sample will be used in section B of this exercise.

    2. **Random sampling:** using random numbers, select a sample of size 10 from the population of 480
       Select a second random sample of size 40 to be used in section B of this exercise.

    3. **Systematic sampling:** choose a starting point at random between 0 and 47 and then choose every 48th item thereafter to form a sample of size 10.

Analysis:
- calculate the mean, μ, and the standard deviation, σ, of the population of 480 accounts
- calculate the mean, $\bar{x}_i$, of each subjective sample of size 10
- calculate the mean, $\bar{y}_i$, of each random sample of size 10
- calculate the mean, $\bar{z}_i$, of each systematic sample
- draw a dot plot of $\bar{x}_i$. Mark μ on the diagram
- draw a dot plot of $\bar{y}_i$. Mark μ on the diagram
- draw a dot plot of $\bar{z}_i$. Mark μ on the diagram

Conclusions:
- are the $\bar{x}$'s good estimators of μ?
- is there evidence of bias?
- are the $\bar{y}$'s good estimators of μ?
- is there evidence of bias?
- are the $\bar{z}$'s good estimators of μ?
- is there evidence of bias?
- compare the estimates of μ for the 3 types of sample
- compare the amount of work involved in each type of sampling
- under what circumstances might the systematic sample give an unsatisfactory estimate of μ?

Section B

Analysis:
- calculate the mean $\bar{a}_i$ for each subjective sample of size 40
- calculate the mean $\bar{b}_i$ for each random sample of size 40

Conclusions:
- are the $\bar{a}$'s good estimators of μ? Is there evidence of bias?
- are the $\bar{b}$'s good estimators of μ? Is there evidence of bias?
- how do the means, $\bar{x}$, of subjective samples size 10 compare with the means, $\bar{a}$, of subjective samples size 40?
- was the extra work involved in taking a larger sample worthwhile?
- how do the means, $\bar{y}$, of random samples size 10 compare with the means, $\bar{b}$, of random samples size 40?
- was the extra work involved in taking a larger sample worthwhile?

Section C

Data collection:
- shops 1 to 5 are in the affluent suburbs – this is the 1st stratum
  shops 6 to 8 are in large rural villages – this is the 2nd stratum
  shops 9 and 10 are in the inner city – this is the 3rd stratum
- **Stratified random sampling:** each student should select a random sample of size 5 from stratum 1, size 3 from stratum 2, and size 2 from stratum 3 to give a sample of size 10

Analysis:
- calculate the mean $\bar{p}_i$ of each stratified sample of size 10
- draw a dot plot of $\bar{p}_i$. Mark μ on the diagram

Conclusions:
- are the $\bar{p}$'s good estimators of μ? Is there evidence of bias?
- compare the results of stratified sampling with those of random sampling
- if you were to take a larger stratified random sample, how would you choose your sample proportions?

Section D

Data collection:
- **Cluster sampling:** each student should select 2 shops at random and then select random samples of size 5 from each to give a sample of size 10

Analysis:
- calculate the mean $\bar{c}_i$ for each cluster sample of size 10
- draw a dot plot of $\bar{c}_i$. Mark μ on the diagram

Conclusions:
- are the $\bar{c}$'s good estimators of μ? Is there evidence of bias?
- compare the results of cluster sampling with those of random sampling

Final conclusions:
- under what circumstances would you choose to use a sample rather than examining the entire population?
- what are the advantages of using a sample?
- which of the five methods of sampling (subjective, random, systematic, stratified random, cluster) gives the most satisfactory estimate of μ?
- what is the likely effect of increasing the sample size on your chosen method?

Extensions:
- collect samples of size 40 for systematic, stratified random and cluster sampling and examine the effect of increasing the sample size
- collect a subjective stratified sample (generally called a quota sample)
- repeat the analysis as given for the sample standard deviations

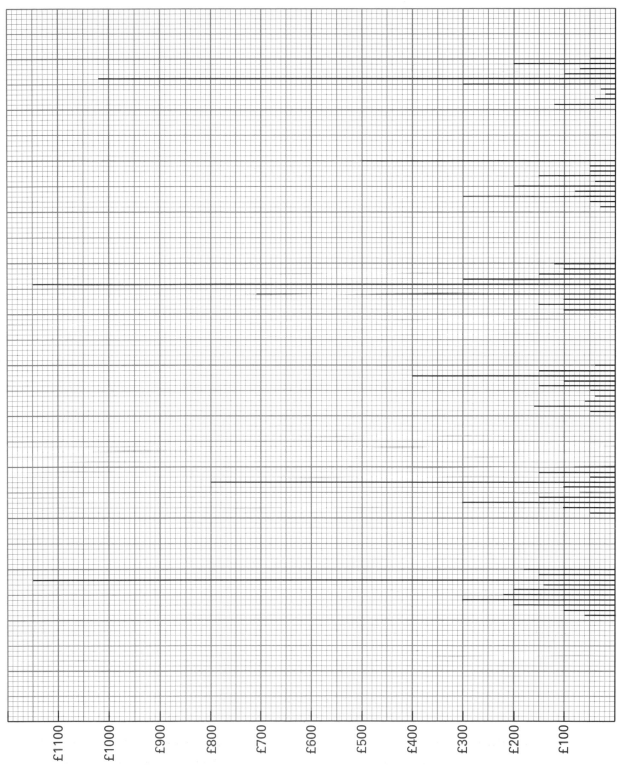

Shop 2

£1100 £1000 £900 £800 £700 £600 £500 £400 £300 £200 £100

Shop 3

£1100 £1000 £900 £800 £700 £600 £500 £400 £300 £200 £100

Shop 4

£1100 £1000 £900 £800 £700 £600 £500 £400 £300 £200 £100

Shop 5

£1100
£1000
£900
£800
£700
£600
£500
£400
£300
£200
£100

Shop 6

£1100 £1000 £900 £800 £700 £600 £500 £400 £300 £200 £100

Shop 7

£1100 £1000 £900 £800 £700 £600 £500 £400 £300 £200 £100

Shop 8

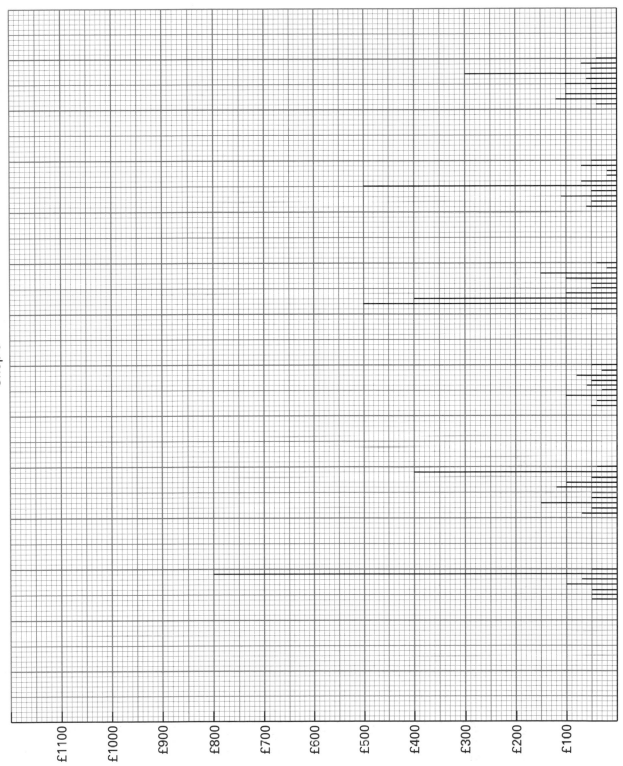

Shop 10

£1100　£1000　£900　£800　£700　£600　£500　£400　£300　£200　£100

1.3 **Volunteers**

This exercise uses a 'test your strength device' but it can also be done using a reaction time ruler, standing long jump, test of memory, etc.

Requirements:
- test your strength device
- class of at least 25 pupils
- class list (ignore absentees)

Data collection:
- using random numbers select, without replacement, 8 names from the class list. These are your x pupils
- explain to the class that you are collecting data for a statistics exercise and describe the task. Then ask for 8 volunteers. Mark these names on the class list. These are your y pupils (there may be some pupils included in both groups)
- administer the test to all the pupils in the class and record the results for each pupil

Analysis:
- calculate the mean μ and standard deviation σ for the whole class (the population)
- calculate the mean and standard deviation for the two samples: $\bar{x}$ and s_x, $\bar{y}$ and s_y
- find the median and quartiles for the population and for each sample
- draw a box and whisker diagram for the population and the two samples on the same page

Conclusions:
- define the population from which the samples are taken
- are your methods of sampling likely to have introduced any bias?
- which sample best represents the population?
- discuss possible bias in the sampling methods

Extensions:
- ask the teacher to select 8 representative pupils before any testing has been done and examine this third sample
- repeat with other classes
- repeat with a learned skill, such as shooting into a netball goal, serving a tennis ball, etc.
- test to see if the y sample comes from a population with mean μ and standard deviation σ

2 Data display and summary statistics

Notes for students

The purpose of the exercises in this chapter is to help students to choose the most appropriate diagram to illustrate a particular set of data. Most of these exercises instruct the student to use more than one diagram to illustrate the same data, so that the diagrams may be compared and their advantages and disadvantages considered. However, the student should be aware that this would not be acceptable in a statistical report, where only the most suitable diagram should be used. It is bad practice to illustrate the same set of data in several different ways except in cases where there is a clearly defined reason for doing so.

When choosing a diagram the first thing to consider is the nature of the data. This will immediately eliminate several possibilities. For example, a histogram is not used for discrete data.

Secondly, consider whether you wish to draw attention to any particular features of the data. For example, a pie chart is good for illustrating proportions and a box and whisker diagram is suitable for showing outliers.

Finally the choice may come down to personal preference. For some sets of data histograms and box and whisker diagrams may be equally acceptable alternatives, just as pie charts, bar charts or bar line diagrams may be suitable for others.

Types of diagram

1. **Bar chart or bar line diagram:** used for both quantitative and qualitative discrete data. Good for comparing the frequency of outcomes, particularly if the differences are small. For qualitative data it can be useful to arrange the classes in order of magnitude (a Pareto chart).

2. **Box and whisker diagram:** used for quantitative data. Shows skewness; outliers can be indicated. Particularly good for comparing two or more sets of data. No means of showing total frequency. May not be suitable for very large or bimodal data sets.

3. **Cumulative frequency curves:** used for quantitative data (a step diagram is used for discrete data). Mainly used for estimating percentiles, quartiles and medians. Better diagrams are available for all other purposes.

4. **Dot plot:** used for quantitative data. Useful for small sets of highly skewed data. Good for comparing two or more sets of data as it shows location, spread and frequency. Similar to box and whisker diagram but shows more details.

5. **Frequency polygon/curve:** used for continuous data. May be easier to read than a histogram when two or more sets of data are superimposed.

6. **Histogram:** used for continuous data. A good general purpose diagram which shows frequency density, range, skewness and mode. Useful for comparison of two or more sets of data if the diagrams are carefully aligned and drawn to the same scale. Does not show the total frequency.

7. **Pie chart:** used for discrete qualitative data. Shows the proportion of data in a particular class. As the area is proportional to the frequency, it can be used to compare the total frequency of two data sets.

8. **Scatter diagram:** used for bivariate quantitative data. See Chapter 10, Bivariate data.

9. **Stem and leaf diagram:** used for quantitative data. Displays the raw data in a 'histogram' type diagram. Not suitable for very large data sets. Back to back stem and leaf diagrams can be used for comparing two data sets.

Summary statistics

1. **Measures of location**
   The **mean** is based on all of the data items which is why it is generally preferred. However, outliers may draw the mean well away from the centre of the data set and then the **median** may be a better measure of location. The median is also used with truncated distributions.

   The **mode** is not affected by outliers.

   Comparison of the mean, median and mode can be used to investigate skewness.

2. **Measures of spread**
   The **standard deviation** is associated with the mean and has the same advantages and disadvantages as the mean.

   The **interquartile range** is associated with the median.

   The **range** can be greatly affected by outliers, but the average range gives a good measure of spread when a large number of small samples are available.

2.1 Father's age at birth of subject

Requirements:
- at least 50 subjects

Data collection:
- ask each subject to give the age, *x*, of his/her father when the subject was born

Analysis:
- gather data into a grouped frequency distribution with about 7 classes. You may wish to use unequal class widths
- draw a histogram of the data
- find the median and interquartile range of *X*
- draw a box and whisker diagram of the data
- calculate the mean and standard deviation of *X*
- find the mode and range of *X*
- display your summary statistics in a table

Conclusions:
- what is the population from which the sample is drawn?
- is your choice of subjects likely to have introduced any bias?
- comment on the distribution, for example average, spread, skewness, outliers
- which diagram best displays this data? (select one diagram)
- which numerical measure best describes this data? (select one average and one measure of spread)

Extensions:
- repeat the exercise for mother's age at birth of subject and compare the two distributions
- use the sign test to test whether the median age of the father at the birth of the child is 25 years old
- if possible, find published data on the average age of father/mother at birth of children and compare with your data
- use a paired *t*-test to examine whether father's age is on average significantly higher than mother's age at the birth of each subject
- examine the age of the father against the position of the child in the family (oldest, youngest, etc.)

2.2   Greek puzzle

In this exercise subjects are timed completing the Greek puzzle on page 21.

As some subjects may find this puzzle difficult, students should do a pilot study first to decide on a 'cut-off' time, such that 80–90% of subjects will complete the puzzle.

Students may wish to pool data for this exercise.

Requirements:
- a copy of the practice puzzle (page 20) and the Greek puzzle (page 21) for each subject
- watch to measure minutes and seconds
- at least 40 subjects

Data collection:
- give each subject a copy of the instructions and the practice puzzle. Allow them time to do the practice puzzle
- give each subject the Greek puzzle and record the time, x, taken to complete it. If necessary stop the subject at the 'cut-off' time

Analysis:
- gather the times, x, into a grouped frequency distribution with about 7 classes. The last class must be $x > \ldots$ and will include all subjects who failed to complete the puzzle
- find the median, interquartile range and mode for this data
- draw a suitable diagram to represent this data

Conclusions:
- what is the population from which the sample is drawn?
- is your choice of subjects likely to have introduced any bias?
- discuss the problems encountered when choosing a suitable diagram to represent your data and justify your choice
- why were you not asked to calculate a mean and standard deviation for this data?
- comment on the suggestion that you should omit data from those subjects who failed to complete the puzzle in the allotted time

Extensions:
- use a sign test to test whether the median time to do the puzzle is 4 minutes
- sample from different strata of the population for comparison, for example, different ages, different gender, science students versus art students, etc.

Practice puzzle for the Greek puzzle

Starting at a compass ( ) on the top row, move to the bottom row as quickly as you can, following the given sequence.

You can move to the left, to the right, up, down or diagonally.

Draw your route on the puzzle.

Start here

The Greek puzzle

Starting at a compass (⊚) on the top row, move to the bottom row as quickly as you can, following the given sequence.

You can move to the left, to the right, up, down or diagonally.

Draw your route on the puzzle.

2.3 Journey times

The data collection for this exercise should be done over a six-week period (longer, if possible).

Requirements:
- watch to measure minutes/seconds

Data collection:
- each student should record the journey time from home to college and the journey time from college to home each day
  For each journey note
  (a) the time of departure
  (b) the day and date
  (c) the weather – decide some categories in advance
  (d) any unusual circumstances which might affect the journey time – for example, accident, roadworks, religious holiday

Analysis:

Diagrams 1:
- gather *all* of the journey times, z, into a grouped frequency distribution (with up to 10 classes). You may wish to vary the class width depending on the frequencies
- gather the journey times *to* college, x, into a grouped frequency distribution
- gather the journey times home *from* college, y, into a grouped frequency distribution
- draw a histogram for the X data
- draw a histogram for the Y data
- draw a histogram for the Z data

Comments:
- comment on the shape of the histogram for Z
  Is it bimodal or unimodal?
  Is it skewed? Are there outliers?
- compare the histograms for X and Y
  Look at average time and variability, as well as the points mentioned for Z above
- do the distributions of X and Y explain any of the features of Z?

Diagrams 2:
- draw a back to back stem and leaf diagram for the distributions of X and Y

Comments:
- are there any features in the data which are better illustrated by the stem and leaf diagram than the histograms (or vice versa)?

Diagrams 3:
- draw up a cumulative frequency distribution for X and for Y
- draw a cumulative frequency curve for X and for Y
- using your cumulative frequency curves find the median, the lower quartile and the upper quartile for each distribution
- draw a box and whisker diagram for X and for Y. Align them one below the other on the same page. Mark any outliers

Comments:
- comment on the shape of each of the box and whisker plots and compare them (see the guidelines given in the comments to diagrams 1)

Numerical measures:
- calculate the mean and standard deviation for each of the distributions of X, Y and Z
- estimate the mode and find the range for each of the three distributions
- complete the following table

	Mean	Standard deviation	Median	Interquartile range	Modal class	Range
X						
Y						
Z						

Conclusions:
- what is the population from which the samples were drawn?
- is your method of sampling likely to have introduced any bias?
- you would normally use only one diagram to illustrate a set of data. Which of the three diagrams best compares the distributions of X and Y?
- which pair of numerical measures best summarises the differences between the distributions of X and Y?
- review your conclusions (with regard to variability and skewness) in the light of the disruptive features listed in the data collection

Extensions:
- pool students' data for journeys to (or from) college and draw box and whisker diagrams for this combined data. On the same page draw box and whisker diagrams for each individual student's data
- are journey times different on different days of the week/in different weather conditions?
- fit Normal (or other) distributions and test for goodness of fit

2.4 Parliamentary elections

Requirements:
- book or CD Rom containing detailed election results

Data collection:
- for the July 1985 by-election in the Brecon and Radnor constituency (or another by-election with a close result)
  record the number or percentage of votes for each party
- from the national figures for the 1992 general election record
  (a) the number of votes for each major party
  (b) the number of seats won by each major party
- for Scotland record the number of votes for each major party
  in the 1992 general election

Analysis:
- draw a bar chart and a pie chart for the Brecon and Radnor data
- for the national data draw
  (a) a pie chart for votes and a pie chart for seats on the same page
  (b) a bar chart for votes and a bar chart for seats on the same page
- draw a pie chart and a bar chart for the votes in Scotland. Draw the area
  of this pie chart to the same scale as the pie chart for the national data

Conclusions:
- for the Brecon and Radnor data, which diagram best illustrates the results?
- for the national data, which type of diagram best illustrates the discrepancy
  between votes cast and seats won?
- for the Scottish data compared with the national data, which type
  of diagram best illustrates the different voting patterns?

Extensions:
- carry out a similar analysis for a country where elections are
  based on proportional representation

2.5 Churchyard

Requirements:
- churchyard or cemetery with a section of old graves (pre-1920) and of new graves (post 1945). You may need to look at two different cemeteries

Data collection:
- record the age at death from 60 old graves. You may record more than one age from some stones
- repeat for 60 new graves

Analysis:
- group the data from the old graves into about 10 groups
- display this data in a stem and leaf diagram (allow room for a second stem and leaf diagram to fit back to back with this one)
- calculate the mean, median and mode of this data
- calculate the quartiles, standard deviation and range of this data
- display this data in a box and whisker diagram (allow room for a second box and whisker diagram on this page)
- repeat this analysis for the data from the new graves. Draw the box and whisker diagram to scale with the one for the old graves and the stem and leaf diagram back to back with the one for the old graves

Conclusions:
- what are the populations from which the samples are drawn?
- is your method of data collection likely to have introduced any bias?
- use your diagrams and calculations to compare and contrast the two sets of data
- which of the diagrams are most helpful in making the comparisons?
- what do the three measures of location indicate about possible changes in longevity?

Extensions:
- repeat the survey for data from the records of deaths from the 15th and 16th centuries
- look for differences in age at death between men and women, between inner city and rural areas, etc.
- compare calculations based on grouped and ungrouped data

2.6 Apples

All the analysis in this exercise should be done using a statistical computer package. At each stage the students should comment on the output. These comments should be *brief* and refer only to general trends (not minor fluctuations).

Requirements:
- computer with a statistical package such as *Minitab*, *Statgraphics*, etc.

Data collection:
- enter the data given below into the program

Analysis:
- draw a scatter diagram to show, for each type of apple, how quantity is related to price
- draw a graph to show, for each type of apple, how price has changed over time
- use the computer program to obtain summary statistics for the data. *Select* suitable summary statistics and quote them to a reasonable degree of accuracy. Use these to compare the three types of apples
- find the total quantity of each type of apple sold over the period
- find the total quantity of apples sold each week
- find the total amount spent on apples each week
- find, for each week, the quantity of type A apples sold as a percentage of the total. Repeat for type B and type C
- draw a graph to show how market shares have altered

Conclusions:
- summarise your main findings, in one paragraph

Extensions:
- use this data to investigate other features of your statistical package such as alternative diagrams, calculations, regression and correlation

The data:

Week	Apple A Price	Apple A Quantity	Apple B Price	Apple B Quantity	Apple C Price	Apple C Quantity
1	63	1010	102	695	148	390
2	66	905	103	684	153	353
3	69	887	101	711	134	357
4	73	942	105	730	146	378
5	68	1047	99	774	164	368
6	76	892	102	792	175	374
7	82	686	89	903	152	389
8	80	691	79	1040	129	392
9	88	549	76	1035	154	361
10	84	567	75	1117	178	372
11	92	499	71	1214	197	349
12	91	489	72	1095	150	362

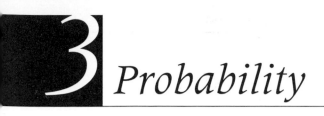

3 Probability

Notes for students

The concept of probability is best illustrated by an example.

If the probability of an event is $\frac{1}{5}$, you would expect that event to occur 1 time in 5 in the long run.

Probability is measured on a scale from 0 to 1 where 0 indicates impossibility and 1 indicates certainty.

Probabilities are usually assigned empirically (that is, based on experiment) or theoretically. Some events can be approached in both ways and in practice it is always found that, with a large number of experiments, the results will be similar.

The laws of probability

These laws are often written using Set notation where:

- 'and' is written as ∩, called Intersection
- 'or' is written as ∪, called Union (meaning event A or event B or both)
- 'not A' is written as $\bar{A}$ or A'

For two events A and B:

- $P(A) + P(A') = 1$
- $P(A \cup B) = P(A) + P(B) - P(A \cap B)$
- $P(A \cap B) = P(A|B) \times P(B)$ or
- $P(A \cap B) = P(B|A) \times P(A)$

If A and B are **independent** events then:

- $P(A|B) = P(A)$
- $P(B|A) = P(B)$
- $P(A \cap B) = P(A) \times P(B)$
  (Any one of these equalities implies the other two.)

If A and B are **mutually exclusive** then:

- $P(A \cap B) = 0$

If A and B are **exhaustive** then:

- $P(A \cup B) = 1$

3.1 **Satellite TV**

Requirements: • 150 subjects (all to be students from your school or college)

Data collection: • ask each subject if they have a satellite TV receiver in their home
• record the results in the order in which they were collected

Analysis: • complete the following table

Number of subjects asked (cumulative), n	5	10	15	20	. . .	150
Number with satellite TV out of n subjects, x						
Proportion of total with satellite TV, $\frac{x}{n}$						

• draw a graph of proportion against the (cumulative) number of subjects asked

Conclusions: • what is the population from which your sample was drawn?
• is your choice of subjects likely to have introduced any bias?
• do the points on your graph lie approximately on a horizontal line?
• do they get nearer to the line as n increases?
• use the line to estimate the proportion of the student population which has satellite TV receivers
• is it reasonable to suppose that your sample is representative of the student population of *(a)* your school or college *(b)* your community *(c)* the UK?

Extensions: • take a sample of 25 teachers and test whether the proportion of teachers having satellite TV is the same as for students
• calculate a confidence interval for the proportion of your student population with satellite TV receivers
• test your student proportion against the population proportion claimed by the promoters of satellite TV

3.2 **Pedestrian-controlled crossing**

In this exercise students will need to work in pairs to collect the data.

Requirements:
- a very busy shopping street with two pedestrian-controlled crossings visible from a single point
- a watch to measure time in seconds

Data collection:
- define a traffic light to be **red** (to the motorist) whenever it is not actually **green** (that is, **red** includes flashing or amber lights)
- students should stand in pairs observing one of the crossings each
- using the same watch or synchronised watches, each student should record the times that the traffic lights on the crossings change colour

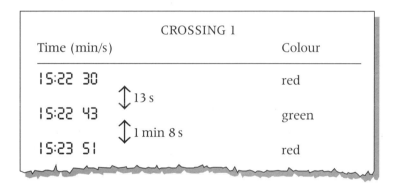

- collect data for at least 15 minutes

Analysis:
- *A* is the event that crossing 1 shows red
  B is the event that crossing 2 shows red
- estimate $P(A) = \dfrac{\text{total length of time crossing 1 is red}}{\text{total length of observation time}}$
- estimate $P(B) = \dfrac{\text{total length of time crossing 2 is red}}{\text{total length of observation time}}$
- similarly estimate, from your data, $P(A \cap B)$, $P(A|B)$, $P(B|A)$, $P(A \cup B)$, $P(A')$, $P(B')$, $P(A' \cap B')$
- verify that
$$P(A) + P(A') = 1$$
$$P(A \cap B) = P(B) \times P(A|B)$$
$$P(A \cap B) = P(A) \times P(B|A)$$
$$P(A \cup B) = P(A) + P(B) - P(A \cap B)$$

Conclusions:
- is the time or place of data collection likely to have affected your results?
- compare $P(A|B)$ with $P(A)$
- compare $P(B|A)$ with $P(B)$
- are *A* and *B* independent events?

Extensions:
- investigate the distribution of the length of time for which the traffic light is red for different times of days or different days of the week
- investigate $P(A)$ at different times of day

3.3 Random numbers

Requirements: • 10 subjects

Data collection: • explain to each subject that, in random number tables, each digit from 0 to 9 is equally likely to appear in each position (you might like to show them a page of random numbers)
• ask each subject to write down 12 digits, x, at random, in 3 blocks of 4

Analysis: • complete the table to form a frequency distribution

x	0	1	...	9
f				

• draw a bar line diagram of the data
• how many of the blocks of 4 begin with a 0?
• how many of the blocks of 4 contain 4 different digits?
• show that, if the numbers are random, the probability of a block of 4 containing all different digits is 0.504
• using all 120 digits (if possible increase this number by pooling data with other students) form a frequency distribution of the number of digits between successive nines, y

y	0	1	2	...
f				

• show that, if the numbers are random, P(6 or fewer digits between successive nines) = 0.52 (to 2 dp)

Conclusions: • what is the population from which the subjects were selected?
• is your choice of subjects likely to have introduced any bias?
• is the distribution of X consistent with the numbers being random?
• is the number of blocks beginning with a 0 consistent with the numbers being random?
• is the number of blocks containing 4 different digits consistent with the numbers being random?
• is the distribution of Y consistent with the numbers being random?

Extensions: • repeat the exercise using random numbers generated by a computer or calculator, or from a table of random digits
• examine the effect of increasing the number of digits from subjects or of generated numbers
• calculate and examine the probabilities of 1 pair, 2 pairs, 3 of a kind, 4 of a kind in blocks of 4 digits
• use χ^2 tests for the Uniform distribution of digits and for the Geometric distribution of digits between successive nines

4 *The Binomial distribution*

Notes for students

If a trial can result in one of two outcomes: 'success' or 'failure', and if the probability of 'success' is p, then the probability of exactly r successes in n independent trials is $^nC_r\,(p)^r\,(1-p)^{n-r}$.

Note 1: The symbol q is often used in place of $1-p$.

Note 2: Either outcome *can* be defined as 'success' but it is conventional to define 'success' so that $p \leqslant 0.5$.

If the random variable R follows a Binomial distribution with parameters n and p, often written $R{\sim}B(n,p)$ then:

- $P(R = r) = {}^nC_r\,(p)^r\,(1-p)^{n-r}$
- $E(R) = np$
- $\mathrm{Var}(R) = np(1-p)$

Example

A recent UK survey claimed that the proportion of women aged between 16 and 30 who do not want to have children is 0.2. Assuming that this claim is correct, the probability that a random sample of 7 women in this age group contains 3 who do not want to have children is

$$^7C_3\,(0.2)^3\,(0.8)^4 = 35\,(0.008)\,(0.4096) = 0.115$$

In random samples of size 7 the mean number who do not want children is $7 \times 0.2 = 1.4$ with a standard deviation of $\sqrt{7 \times 0.2 \times 0.8} = \sqrt{1.12} = 1.06$

Note 3: the Binomial model assumes the following conditions:

1. There is a fixed number of trials.

2. There are exactly two possible outcomes of each trial.

3. The trials are independent.

4. The probability of 'success' is the same for each trial.

You must consider whether these conditions are likely to apply before you fit a Binomial model.

4.1 Darts

This project could apply to almost any sporting activity that involves hitting a target: e.g. putting in golf, serving a tennis ball, scoring a goal at hockey or football, etc.

Requirements:
- one subject
- a dart board and darts
- a measuring tape to measure the throwing distance from the board, or a mat with the distances marked on it

Data collection:
- conduct a pilot study to determine a suitable throwing distance so that the proportion of darts landing in the target area of the board is between 0.1 and 0.5. In the case of an expert darts player it may be necessary to reduce the target area
- decide how to record darts which fail to stick in the board
- throw 9 darts and record the number, x, which land in the target area
- repeat 30–50 times, recording your results in order. All throws are to be made by the same person

Analysis:
- gather your data into a frequency distribution

x	0	1	2	...	9
Observed f					

- calculate $\bar{x}$
- use $\bar{x}$ as an estimate of $E(X) = np$, where $n = 9$, to estimate p
- calculate the distribution of expected frequencies based on $X \sim B(9,p)$
- draw bar line diagrams of observed frequencies and of expected frequencies either aligned one below the other or on the same axes

Conclusions:
- what is the population from which your sample is drawn?
- is your method of sampling likely to have introduced any bias?
- does your data fit a Binomial model?
- does your data suggest that the probability of throwing a dart into the target area is constant?
- does your data suggest that the trials are independent?

Extensions:
- calculate the standard deviation of the observed data and compare this to $\sqrt{np(1-p)}$
- test for goodness of fit
- repeat this exercise throwing from a different distance, using a different hand, subject, or target area, etc. Test whether the difference in the values of p obtained is significant

4.2 **Weighted containers**

If two identical weights are lifted, one after the other, the second is usually judged to be heavier than the first.

Requirements:
- 5 pairs of weighted containers, each pair identical in shape and weight and labelled A and B; for example, large matchboxes, sweet tubes or jam jars. Each pair should have a different weight to any other pair
- a minimum of 30 subjects

Data collection:
- tell the first subject to lift container A and replace it, then to lift container B and replace it and to state which container is the heavier. Encourage a quick response – insist that the subject makes a choice
- record whether container A or B is judged the heavier
- repeat for the other pairs of containers
- record the number of times, *x* (out of 5), that the first container (A) is chosen
- repeat for the other subjects

Analysis:
- gather your data into a frequency distribution

x	0	1	2	3	4	5
Observed *f*						

- calculate $\bar{x}$
- use $\bar{x}$ as an estimate of $E(X) = np$ where $n = 5$ to estimate p
- calculate the distribution of expected frequencies based on $X \sim B(5,p)$
- draw bar line diagrams of observed frequencies and of expected frequencies either aligned one below the other or on the same axes

Conclusions:
- what is the population from which the sample is drawn?
- is your choice of subjects likely to have introduced any bias?
- what does your estimated value of *p* suggest about the perception of weight?
- does your data fit a Binomial model?
- does your data suggest that the probability of choosing the second weight as the heavier is the same for all subjects?
- does your data suggest that all trials are independent?

Extensions:
- calculate the standard deviation of the observed data and compare this to $\sqrt{np(1-p)}$
- test for goodness of fit
- fit a Binomial model with $p = 0.5$
- does the order of presentation affect the results, e.g. A before B or B before A, or lighter pairs presented before heavier pairs?
- are girls' results different to boys' results?
- how are results affected if pairs are not *exactly* the same weight? How large a difference is necessary to make $p = 0.5$?
- consider the weights chosen. Does the magnitude of the weights affect the results?

4.3 Number recall

In this exercise, 8-digit numbers are read aloud, some as two blocks of 4 digits and some as a block of 8 digits. The subjects write down each number as accurately as possible from memory immediately after they have heard it.

Requirements:
- a list of 20 8-digit random numbers
- one answer sheet per subject

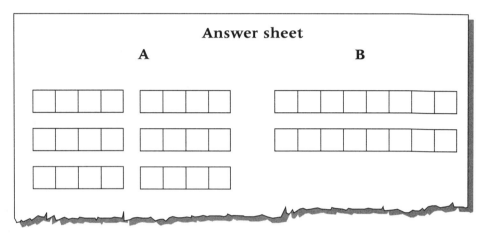

- about 20 subjects, similar in age and in numerical skills

Data collection:
- conduct a pilot study to ensure that writing 8-digit numbers has a probability of error of between 0.1 and 0.5 for your group of subjects. It may be necessary to adjust the number of digits to be used
- read the first number as two blocks of 4 digits, with a short pause between the blocks. Ask the subjects to write down the number on the answer sheet in the column labelled A
- repeat for the next 9 numbers
- read the remaining numbers each as one block of 8 digits, to be written in the column labelled B

Analysis:
- for each subject record x, the number of incorrectly written 8-digit numbers in column A (out of 10) and record y, the number of incorrectly written 8-digit numbers in column B (out of 10)
- gather your X data into a frequency distribution

x	0	1	2	...	8 or more
Observed f					

- calculate $\bar{x}$
- use $\bar{x}$ as an estimate of $E(X) = np_x$ where $n = 10$ to estimate p_x
- calculate the distribution of expected frequencies based on $X \sim B(10, p_x)$

- draw bar line diagrams of observed frequencies and of expected frequencies either aligned one below the other or on the same axes
- repeat the analysis for your Y data, labelling all diagrams and tables carefully

Conclusions:
- what is the population from which the subjects were drawn?
- is your choice of subjects likely to have introduced any bias?
- does $B(10,p_x)$ provide an adequate model for the distribution of X?
- does the X data indicate that the probability of error in this exercise is the same for all subjects tested?
- does the X data indicate that the trials are independent?
- does $B(10,p_y)$ provide an adequate model for the distribution of Y?
- does the Y data indicate that the probability of error in this exercise is the same for all subjects tested?
- does the Y data indicate that the trials are independent?
- compare p_x and p_y

Extensions:
- calculate the standard deviations of X and Y and compare them to $\sqrt{np_x(1 - p_x)}$ and $\sqrt{np_y(1 - p_y)}$ respectively
- test X and Y for goodness of fit
- test the hypothesis that the proportion of errors is the same for both presentation methods
- does the method of presentation affect the results e.g. reading 4-digit blocks before 8-digit blocks, or reading 4 blocks of 2 digits?
- are girls' results different from boys' results? Compare different age groups, or mathematicians and non-mathematicians
- test for correlation between method A and method B
- use the paired t-test or the sign test to test for differences between method A and method B
- calculate a confidence interval for $p_y - p_x$

4.4 **Electoral register**

Requirements:
- a copy of a local electoral register, available from public libraries. For the purpose of this exercise an out-of-date register is adequate

Data collection:
- use random numbers to select a starting point
- record the number, x, of the next 20 surnames that begin with a vowel
- repeat 70 times with consecutive blocks of surnames
- repeat the data collection but this time select only the surname of the *first* person listed at each address. Call this variable Y
- repeat 70 times with consecutive blocks of 20 addresses

Analysis:
- gather your X data into a frequency distribution

x	0	1	2	...	15 or more
Observed f					

- calculate $\bar{x}$
- use $\bar{x}$ as an estimate of $E(X) = np_x$ where $n = 20$ to estimate p_x
- calculate the distribution of expected frequencies based on $X \sim B(20, p_x)$
- draw bar line diagrams of observed frequencies and of expected frequencies either aligned one below the other or on the same axes
- repeat the analysis for your Y data, labelling all diagrams and tables carefully

Conclusions:
- what is the population from which the sample is drawn?
- is your method of sampling likely to have introduced any bias?
- does $B(20, p_x)$ provide an adequate model for the distribution of X?
- does the X data indicate that the event of a surname beginning with a vowel is independent for each member of the sample?
- does $B(20, p_y)$ provide an adequate model for the distribution of Y?
- does the Y data indicate that the event of a surname beginning with a vowel is independent for each member of the sample?
- suggest a possible reason for the differences in the two distributions

Extensions:
- calculate the standard deviations of X and Y and compare to $\sqrt{np_x(1 - p_x)}$ and $\sqrt{np_y(1 - p_y)}$ respectively
- test X and Y for goodness of fit
- repeat the Y experiment using a register based on a (possibly) different population (e.g. a register from the 1930s or a constituency from another region) and test for differences in p_y

4.5 Multiple choice quiz

The quiz used should be such that all subjects should be able to answer some, but not all, of the questions without guessing. You may wish to conduct a pilot study to check the suitability of your quiz.

Requirements:
- a quiz consisting of 10 multiple choice questions each with 4 options (one correct option per question)
- 2 answer sheets per subject, numbered in pairs for identification

Circle your choice.	Candidate no._____
1. A B C D	6. A B C D
2. A B C D	7. A B C D
3. A B C D	

- minimum of 30 subjects, each given a candidate number

Data collection:
- ask subjects to complete an answer sheet by circling one option for each question. At this stage they have not seen the questions so they must guess which is the correct answer. Label this sheet 'guess'
- give the subjects the questions and ask them to complete another answer sheet by circling the option which they believe to be correct. Label this sheet 'answer'

Analysis:
- collect the 'guess' sheets and count the number, x, of correct answers on each sheet
- gather your X data into a frequency distribution

x	0	1	2	3	4	5 or more
Observed f						

- calculate the distribution of expected frequencies based on $X \sim B(10, 0.25)$
- draw bar line diagrams of observed frequencies and of expected frequencies either aligned one below the other or on the same axes
- collect the 'answer' sheets and count the number, y, of correct answers on each sheet
- gather your Y data into a frequency distribution

y	0	1	2	...	10
Observed f					

- calculate $\bar{y}$
- use $\bar{y}$ as an estimate of $E(Y) = np$ where $n = 10$ to estimate p_y
- calculate the distribution of expected frequencies based on $Y \sim B(10, p_y)$
- draw bar line diagrams of observed frequencies and of expected frequencies either aligned one below the other or on the same axes

Conclusions:
- what is the population from which your sample was drawn?
- is your method of sampling likely to have introduced any bias?
- does $B(10, 0.25)$ provide an adequate model for the distribution of X?
- does the X data suggest that each guess is independent with $p_x = 0.25$?
- does $B(10, p_y)$ provide an adequate model for the distribution of Y?
- does the Y data suggest that the probability of a question being answered correctly is constant?
- compare $E(X)$ to $\bar{x}$ and $\bar{y}$

Extensions:
- calculate the standard deviation of X and Y and compare to the relevant $\sqrt{np(1-p)}$
- test X and Y for goodness of fit
- calculate the product–moment correlation coefficient between X and Y
- use a paired t-test or sign test to test whether the average score is higher for the answers than for the 'guessed' answers
- calculate a confidence interval for the mean of the distribution of $Y - X$
- test whether there is a difference between the proportion of correct answers to Question 1 and the proportion of correct answers to Question 10 (or any other pair of questions)

5 The Poisson distribution

Notes for students

If events occur independently and at random, at a constant average rate of λ per unit time/space, then the probability of exactly r events occurring in a particular unit of time/space is $e^{-\lambda}\dfrac{\lambda^r}{r!}$

If the random variable R follows a Poisson distribution with parameter λ, often written $R \sim \text{Po}(\lambda)$, then

- $P(R = r) = e^{-\lambda}\dfrac{\lambda^r}{r!}$

- $E(R) = \lambda$
- $\text{Var}(R) = \lambda$

Example

A botanist claims that the common spotted orchid in Connemara occurs randomly in peat bogs at an average rate of 2 per square metre. Assuming that this claim is correct, the probability that a particular square metre of bog contains exactly 3 of these orchids is

$$e^{-2}\frac{2^3}{3!} = \frac{(0.1353) \times 8}{6} = 0.180$$

The standard deviation of the number of orchids in a square metre of Connemara peat bog is $\sqrt{2}$.

Note: the Poisson model assumes the following conditions:

1. The events occur at random in continuous space or time.

2. Events occur singly, that is, the probability of two events occurring simultaneously is zero.

3. Events occur uniformly, that is, the expected number of events in a given interval is proportional to the size of the interval.

4. Events occur independently.

You must consider whether these conditions are likely to apply before you fit a Poisson model.

5.1 The personal column

This exercise is based on death notices collected from a weekly newspaper (Sundays or local press). It could equally well be done on births, marriages, in memoriam, etc. If the weekly mean is greater than about 10, students may wish to restrict the categories, for example to deaths under 50 years of age.

Requirements:
- one year's newspapers (50 observations). This should be available from a large local library

Data collection:
- record x, the number of death notices each week

Analysis:
- gather your data into a frequency distribution

x	0	1	...
Observed f			

- calculate $\bar{x}$ and s^2
- calculate the distribution of expected frequencies based on $X \sim \mathrm{Po}(\bar{x})$
- draw bar line diagrams of expected frequencies and observed frequencies either aligned one below the other or on the same axes

Conclusions:
- what is the population from which the sample is drawn?
- is your method of sampling likely to have introduced any bias?
- compare the mean and the variance of X
- does the data fit a Poisson model?
- does the data support the view that the mean number of death notices per week is constant throughout the year?

Extensions:
- collect data from a daily paper. Are the results likely to be affected by not having the paper published on Sunday?
- test for goodness of fit

5.2 Spot the difference quiz

Students may wish to do a pilot study to decide on a suitable length of time for this quiz.

Requirements:
- one pair of 'Spot the Difference' pictures with at least 10 differences (more than can be found in the allotted time)
- 30 to 50 subjects
- a watch to measure seconds

Data collection:
- distribute quiz papers to subjects and instruct them to spot and circle as many differences as possible in the time allowed
- mark the quizzes, recording the number of differences spotted correctly, x
- record the number of errors, y (wrongly circled parts of the picture)

Analysis:
- gather your X data into a frequency distribution

x	0	1	2	...
Observed f				

- calculate $\bar{x}$ and s_x^2
- calculate the distribution of expected frequencies based on $X \sim \mathrm{Po}(\bar{x})$
- draw bar line diagrams of expected frequencies and observed frequencies either aligned one below the other or on the same axes
- repeat the analysis for the distribution of Y

Conclusions:
- what is the population from which your sample is drawn?
- is your choice of subjects likely to have introduced any bias?
- compare the mean and the variance for X
- does the X data fit a Poisson model?
- does the X data indicate that the differences are spotted independently and at a constant average rate?
- compare the mean and the variance of Y
- does the Y data fit a Poisson model?
- does the Y data indicate that the errors are made independently and at a constant average rate?

Extensions:
- test for goodness of fit
- is there any relationship between X and Y?

5.3 Pedestrian crossing

Requirements:
- a fairly busy pedestrian crossing
- a data collection sheet
- a watch

Data collection:
- do a pilot study in order to choose a suitable time interval as follows: count the number of people arriving singly at the crossing in 5 minutes; choose an interval based on this data in which an average of about 5 singles would be expected to arrive
- count the number of people arriving singly, x, at the crossing for 30–50 intervals. (If the data is collected over a period of several days it should be collected at roughly the same time of day. Busy times and quiet times should not be mixed)
- count the number of *groups* of people arriving, y, at the crossing for the same 30–50 time intervals (mother + child, friends, etc.)

Analysis:
- gather the X data into a frequency distribution

x	0	1	2	...
Observed f				

- calculate $\bar{x}$, s_x^2
- calculate the distribution of expected frequencies based on $X \sim Po(\bar{x})$
- draw bar line diagrams of expected frequencies and observed frequencies either aligned one below the other or on the same axes
- repeat the analysis for the distribution of Y
- for each interval, evaluate z, the sum of x and y
- repeat the analysis for Z

Conclusions:
- what is the population from which your sample is drawn?
- is your method of sampling likely to have introduced any bias?
- compare the mean and variance for X
- does the X data fit a Poisson model?
- does the X data support the idea that singles arrive at the crossing independently and at a constant average rate?
- consider the above questions for the Y data and for the Z data
- discuss the likely effect on the results if each member of a group were counted as a single

Extensions:
- test for goodness of fit
- repeat for different times of day. Use a contingency table to test whether the ratio of groups to singles arriving at the crossing is independent of the time of day chosen
- test for difference of means

5.4 **Supermarket**

Requirements:
- supermarket at a quiet time and a busy time
- data collection sheet
- a watch

Data collection:
- do a pilot study during a busy time in order to choose a suitable time interval: count the number of shoppers entering the supermarket in 5 minutes. Choose an interval, based on this data, in which an average of about 5 shoppers would be expected to arrive (a family group counts as 1 shopper).
- record the number of shoppers, x, arriving at the supermarket for 30–50 time intervals during the busy time
- record the number of shoppers, y, arriving at the supermarket for 30–50 time intervals during the quiet time

Analysis:
- gather your X data into a frequency distribution

x	0	1	2	...
Observed f				

- calculate $\bar{x}$ and s_x^2
- calculate the distribution of expected frequencies based on $X \sim \text{Po}(\bar{x})$
- draw bar line diagrams of the expected frequencies and the observed frequencies either aligned one below the other or on the same axes
- repeat the analysis for the distribution of Y
- gather *all* of the data, Z, into a frequency distribution. That is, Z is the X and Y data combined
- repeat the analysis for the distribution of Z. Draw all diagrams to the same scale

Conclusions:
- what is the population from which the samples are drawn?
- is your method of sampling likely to have introduced any bias?
- compare the mean and variance of X
- does the X data fit a Poisson distribution?
- does the X data support the view that the rate at which shoppers enter the supermarket is constant at the busy time?
- consider the above questions for the Y data
- compare the observed Z data to the observed X and observed Y data
- compare the mean and variance of Z
- does the Z data fit a Poisson distribution? If not, suggest a reason why not
- discuss the likely effect on the results if all of the persons entering the supermarket had been counted (as opposed to counting a family group as one person)

Extensions:
- test for goodness of fit
- repeat the exercise, counting all the persons entering the supermarket
- repeat the exercise, counting shoppers leaving during the busy time

5.5 Arrivals and departures

This exercise is written for use at an underground station. It could equally well be used at a reasonably busy bus stop or railway station. Data collection may need to be spread over several days.

Requirements:
- data collection sheets
- a watch

Data collection:
- do a pilot study in order to choose a suitable time interval: count the number of people *entering* the station in a 5 minute period; based on this data, choose an interval in which an average of about 5–10 people would be expected to enter
- count the number of people entering the station, *x*, for 30–50 intervals. Data collection should take place at roughly the same time of day. Rush hour and non-rush hour should not be mixed, nor should weekends and weekdays
- count the number of people *leaving* the station, *y*, using the same interval and at the same time of day

Analysis:
- gather the *X* data into a frequency distribution

x	0	1	2	...
Observed *f*				

- calculate $\bar{x}$ and s_x^2
- calculate the distribution of expected frequencies based on $X \sim Po(\bar{x})$
- draw bar line diagrams of the expected frequencies and the observed frequencies either aligned one below the other or on the same axes
- repeat for the *Y* data

Conclusions:
- what is the population from which the sample is drawn?
- is your method of sampling likely to have introduced any bias?
- compare the mean and variance of *X*
- does the *X* data fit a Poisson distribution?
- does the *X* data support the view that the arrivals at the station are independent of one another?
- repeat for the *Y* data

Extensions:
- test for goodness of fit
- collect data at a different time of day and compare the means
- collect arrival data for a different time of day and test for goodness of fit to a Poisson distribution
- collect arrival data for mixed rush hour and non-rush hour and test for goodness of fit to a Poisson distribution

6 The Normal distribution

Notes for students

The Normal distribution arises frequently in practice. It is a symmetrical, bell-shaped distribution of a continuous random variable X, often written $X \sim N(\mu, \sigma^2)$ with a probability density function

$$f(x) = \frac{1}{\sigma \sqrt{2\pi}} e^{-(x-\mu)^2/2\sigma^2} \qquad -\infty < x < +\infty$$

where μ is the mean and σ is the standard deviation.

Probabilities are found, as usual, by integrating $f(x)$. However, it is simpler to use tables of the standard Normal distribution $Z \sim N(0, 1)$ where $z = \dfrac{x - \mu}{\sigma}$

Distribution of sample means (The Central Limit Theorem)

If $\bar{x}$ is the mean of a random sample of size n, drawn from a population with mean μ and variance σ^2, then

(i) $\bar{X}$, the distribution of sample means, will have mean μ and variance $\dfrac{\sigma^2}{n}$ and

(ii) $\bar{X}$ will be approximately Normally distributed, whatever the parent population, provided that n is reasonably large.

It is this result which makes the Normal distribution so important in practice.

Combination of random variables

For two random variables X and Y:

(i) $E(X \pm Y) = E(X) \pm E(Y)$

(ii) If X and Y are independent then
$\text{Var}(X \pm Y) = \text{Var}(X) + \text{Var}(Y)$

(iii) If X and Y are independent and Normally distributed $X \sim N(\mu_x, \sigma_x^2)$ and $Y \sim N(\mu_y, \sigma_y^2)$ then $X \pm Y \sim N(\mu_x \pm \mu_y, \sigma_x^2 + \sigma_y^2)$

6.1 Guessing height

Most people think of height in feet and inches. The use of centimetres here is deliberate.

Requirements:
- 75 subjects
- a metre rule

Data collection:
- show each subject the metre rule and say:
  'This is 100 cm. Guess my height to the nearest centimetre'.
  Encourage the subjects to improve on a guess to the nearest 5 cm

Analysis:
- calculate the mean, $\bar{x}$, and the standard deviation, s
- gather the data into a grouped frequency distribution with at least 7 classes. Choose the classes so that $\bar{x}$ is (approximately) in the centre of a class
- calculate the distribution of expected frequencies based on $X \sim N(\bar{x}, s^2)$
- draw histograms of the observed frequencies and the expected frequencies either aligned one below the other or on the same axes

Conclusions:
- what is the population from which the sample is drawn?
- is your choice of subjects likely to have introduced any bias?
- does your data fit a Normal model? Consider outliers and/or skewness
- compare $\bar{x}$ with your actual height

Extensions:
- test for goodness of fit
- test the hypothesis that the mean of X equals your actual height
- are some groups better at guessing? For example, compare boys/girls, adults/children. Consider both accuracy and consistency
- repeat the exercise without using a metre rule
- repeat the exercise asking subjects to guess your height, Y, in feet and inches. Test for the difference of means and difference of variance for X and Y

6.2 **Weights**

You will need to decide to what level of accuracy you will make the measurements of weight. Students can share the data collection, which may need to be done over a long period.

Requirements:
- scales suitable for weighing bottles of milk
- 100 bottles of milk (or any drink bottled in glass bottles)

Data collection:
- weigh the full bottle of milk, x (with or without the bottle top)
- when the bottle is empty, rinse, dry and weigh the bottle, y
- calculate the weight of the contents of the bottle, z ($z = x - y$)
- record x, y and z for each bottle

Analysis:
- gather the X data into a grouped frequency distribution with at least 7 classes. Choose the classes so that $\bar{x}$ is approximately in the centre of a class
- calculate the mean, $\bar{x}$, and the standard deviation, s_x
- calculate the distribution of expected frequencies based on $X \sim N(\bar{x}, s_x^2)$
- draw histograms of the observed frequencies and the expected frequencies either aligned one below the other or on the same axes
- repeat the analysis for the Y data and the Z data

Conclusions:
- what is the population from which your data is drawn?
- is your method of sampling likely to have introduced any bias?
- does each set of data fit a Normal model?
- how are $\bar{x}$, $\bar{y}$, and $\bar{z}$ related?
- which two of the variables X, Y and Z would you expect to be independent?
- does the relationship between s_x^2, s_y^2 and s_z^2 confirm this?
- do all of your results confirm your knowledge of the distribution of the sum of independent normal random variables?

Extensions:
- test for goodness of fit

6.3 Estimating length

Requirements:
- 50 parallel lines of exactly 25 cm ruled on unlined A4 paper – approximately 6 lines per sheet

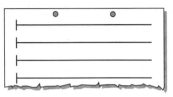

- at least 50 subjects

Data collection:
- showing one line at a time, ask each subject to mark a point 17 cm from the left hand end of the line
- when all 50 lines have been marked, fold under the right-hand side of the paper so that the marks cannot be seen
- again showing one line at a time, ask the subjects to mark a point 7 cm from the left-hand end of the line. Each subject may mark both distances but not on the same line
- for each line measure the first estimate, x, and the second estimate y. Measure or calculate the difference in the two measurements, d
- record x, y and d for each line

Analysis:
- calculate the mean, $\bar{x}$, and the standard deviation, s_x
- gather the X data into a grouped frequency distribution with at least 7 classes. Choose the classes so that $\bar{x}$ is approximately in the centre of a class
- calculate the distribution of expected frequencies based on $X \sim N(\bar{x}, s_x^2)$
- draw histograms of the observed frequencies and the expected frequencies either aligned one below the other or on the same axes
- repeat the analysis for the Y data and the D data

Conclusions:
- what is the population from which the sample is drawn?
- is your choice of subjects likely to have introduced any bias?
- does each set of data fit a Normal model?
- how are $\bar{x}$, $\bar{y}$, and $\bar{d}$ related?
- which two of the variables X, Y and D would you expect to be independent?
- does the relationship between s_x^2, s_y^2 and s_d^2 confirm this?
- do all of your results confirm your knowledge of the distribution of the difference of independent Normal random variables?
- are the subjects better at guessing 17 cm or 7 cm?

Extensions:
- test each distribution for goodness of fit
- test the hypothesis $\mu_x = 17$
- test the hypothesis $\mu_y = 7$
- test whether the variability of X is equal to the variability of Y using the F-test
- calculate confidence intervals for μ_x and μ_y
- calculate confidence intervals for σ_x and σ_y

6.4 Dice

In the analysis tables for Y should be presented together, and the diagrams for Y should be drawn on the same axes. The same applies to the X data.

Requirements:
- 2 white and 1 yellow dice for each subject (any two different colours will do)
- at least 5 subjects (yourself plus 4 additional subjects)
- data collection sheet – a tally chart may be useful

Data collection:
- throw the 3 dice
- record the score on the yellow die, y
- record the mean score of all three dice, $\bar{x}$
- each subject is to repeat the above 75–100 times

Analysis of the observed data:

For your own data:

1. **For the yellow die**
   - gather the data into a frequency distribution
   - add a row to the table for relative frequency ($f/\Sigma f$)
   - draw a bar line diagram of the score, y, using relative frequency
   - calculate the mean and the standard deviation

2. **For the mean score of all 3 dice**
   - gather the data into a frequency distribution
   - add a row to the table for relative frequency ($f/\Sigma f$)
   - draw a bar line diagram of the mean score, $\bar{x}$, using relative frequency
   - calculate the mean and the standard deviation of $\bar{X}$

3. **Repeat 1 and 2 combining results from all five subjects**

Analysis of the theoretical distribution:
- assuming that the dice are fair, draw up a probability distribution for Y
- draw a bar line diagram of Y using probability (instead of relative frequency)
- calculate $E(Y)$ and $Var(Y)$
- complete the following table

$\bar{x}$	1	$\frac{4}{3}$	$\frac{5}{3}$	2	$\frac{7}{3}$	$\frac{8}{3}$	3	$\frac{10}{3}$	$\frac{11}{3}$	4	$\frac{13}{3}$	$\frac{14}{3}$	5	$\frac{16}{3}$	$\frac{17}{3}$	6
$P(\bar{x})$			0.028	0.046	0.069	0.097	0.116	0.125	0.125	0.116	0.097					

- draw a bar line diagram of $\bar{X}$ using probability
- using the table, calculate $E(\bar{X})$ and $Var(\bar{X})$

Conclusions:
- compare the 3 diagrams for the distribution of Y, noting which diagram of observed data is closer to that for the theoretical data
- compare the means and standard deviations of Y with $E(Y)$ and $\sqrt{Var(Y)}$
- similarly, compare the diagrams, means and standard deviations for the distribution of $\bar{X}$
- compare the shape of the distributions of $\bar{X}$ and Y
- compare the mean(s) of $\bar{X}$ with the mean(s) of Y
- compare the standard deviation(s) of $\bar{X}$ and Y
- interpret your results in the light of the Central Limit Theorem

Extensions:
- repeat using more dice
- perform goodness of fit tests for the two distributions (Uniform and Normal)

6.5 Pennies

Requirements:
- accurate scientific scales
- about 90 pennies of varying ages and condition, selected at random, to be representative of the pennies in circulation

Data collection:
- weigh each penny carefully and record the weight, x

Analysis:
- calculate the mean, $\bar{x}$, and standard deviation, s
- gather the data into a grouped frequency distribution (with at least 7 groups). Choose the classes so that $\bar{x}$ is approximately in the centre of a class
- calculate the distribution of expected frequencies based on $X \sim N(\bar{x}, s^2)$
- draw histograms of the observed frequencies and the expected frequencies either aligned one below the other or on the same axes
- using your values of $\bar{x}$ and s, estimate the mean and the standard deviation of a bag of 100 pennies (assume that the bag has no weight)
- calculate an interval within which 90% of bags of 100 pennies would lie
- calculate intervals (90%) for 99 pennies and for 101 pennies

Conclusions:
- what is the population from which the sample is drawn?
- is your method of sampling likely to have introduced any bias?
- does the distribution of the weight of a penny fit a Normal model?
- banks confirm that a bag contains 100 pennies by weight rather than by counting. If a bank uses the interval which you have calculated, is it likely that they would accept bags with too few or too many pennies?

Extensions:
- test the distribution, X, for goodness of fit
- examine the distribution of the weights of bags and include this in your calculations
- compare weights of new pennies and old pennies

Confidence intervals

Notes for students

A sample statistic may be used to estimate a population parameter. For example, the sample mean, $\bar{x}$, may be used to estimate the population mean, μ. However, $\bar{x}$ will not be exactly equal to μ, and so it is sensible to estimate μ by an interval centred on $\bar{x}$ called a **confidence interval**. It has an associated percentage to indicate how confident we are that the interval contains μ. If a large number of samples are taken and a 95% confidence interval is calculated from each, about 95% of these intervals will contain μ. Note that μ remains the same but each sample leads to a different interval. Confidence intervals are most commonly calculated for means, but may also be calculated for proportions, standard deviations, etc. Calculations *always* assume that the samples are random.

Confidence interval for the mean, μ, of a Normal distribution

1. When the standard deviation σ is known, a $(100 - \alpha)$% interval is found by $\bar{x} \pm z_{\alpha/2}\sigma/\sqrt{n}$.
   In practice σ is never known exactly, but in many situations past experience may give a very good estimate.
   An estimate of standard deviation, calculated from a sample, will not be completely accurate but it will enable an approximate interval to be calculated.
   Note: the larger the sample, the better the estimate.
   Even if the parent population is not known to be Normal, the Central Limit Theorem states that the distribution of sample means is approximately Normal, so the interval will be quite accurate.

   #### EXAMPLE
   The weight of eggs from a particular farm is known to be Normally distributed with standard deviation, σ, of 4 grams. A random sample of size 10 has a mean weight, $\bar{x}$, of 58.3 grams.
   A 95% confidence interval for the population mean weight, μ, is $58.3 \pm 1.96 \times 4/\sqrt{10}$, that is (55.8, 60.8).

2. When the standard deviation σ is not known, a $(100 - \alpha)$% interval is found by

   $$\bar{x} \pm t_{\alpha/2,\, n-1}\, \hat{\sigma}/\sqrt{n}, \text{ where } \hat{\sigma}^2 = \frac{\Sigma(x - \bar{x})^2}{n - 1}$$

   #### EXAMPLE
   A sample of 8 fish taken from a pond had a mean weight, $\bar{x}$, of 960 grams with standard deviation $\hat{\sigma}$ of 94 grams.
   A 90% confidence interval for the population mean weight, μ, is $960 \pm 1.895 \times 94/\sqrt{8}$; that is, (897, 1023).
   The sample is assumed to be random. The distribution is also assumed to be Normal but, because of the Central Limit Theorem, this assumption is not of major importance.

Confidence interval for a population proportion, p

It is possible, but difficult, to calculate an exact interval for the population proportion. An approximate interval can be calculated using the Normal approximation to the Binomial distribution. Suppose that of a random sample of n items from a population, r have a particular characteristic. Then an approximate $(100 - \alpha)$% confidence interval for the proportion, p, of the population with this characteristic is

$$\hat{p} \pm z_{\alpha/2}\sqrt{\frac{\hat{p}(1 - \hat{p})}{n}}, \text{ where } \hat{p} = \frac{r}{n}.$$

EXAMPLE
A random sample of 120 books was selected from a school library. During the past month, 27 of them had been borrowed.
An approximate 95% confidence interval for the proportion of books, p, borrowed from this library during the past month is

$$0.225 \pm 1.96\sqrt{\frac{0.225\,(0.775)}{120}}; \text{ that is, } (0.150, 0.300).$$

7.1 **Ear lobes**

Requirements: • about 50 subjects

Data collection: • record for each subject, in order, whether the ear lobes are attached or not attached

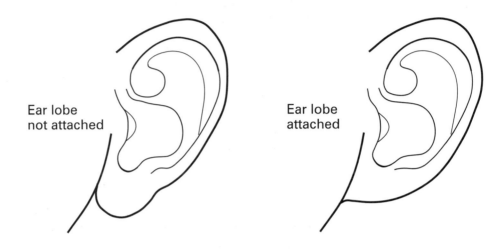

Ear lobe
not attached

Ear lobe
attached

Analysis: • complete the following table:

Number of subjects asked (cumulative), n	10	20	30	40	50
Number with attached ear lobes out of n subjects, r					
Proportion of total with attached ear lobes, $\frac{r}{n}$					

   • calculate an approximate 95% confidence interval for p, the proportion in the population with attached ear lobes, based on the first 10 subjects
   • repeat for the first 20 subjects, 30 subjects, etc.

Conclusions: • what is the population from which the sample is drawn?
   • is your choice of subjects likely to have introduced any bias?
   • why is this an 'approximate' confidence interval?
   • what effect does increasing the sample size have on the width of the confidence interval?

Extensions: • compare confidence intervals calculated for different groups (boys/girls, ethnic groups, etc.)
   • calculate a confidence interval for the difference of proportions for different groups

7.2   Reading glasses

Requirements:
- two groups of 50 subjects from two distinct age groups. For example 15–25 year olds and 40–60 year olds *or* 6–9 year olds and 15–18 year olds

Data collection:
- for each subject in the younger group, record whether the subject needs to wear glasses for reading
- repeat for the older group

Analysis:
- calculate p_{s1}, the proportion of the younger sample who wear glasses for reading
- estimate a 90% confidence interval for p_1, the proportion of this population who wear glasses for reading
- calculate p_{s2}, the proportion of the older sample who wear glasses for reading
- estimate a 90% confidence interval for p_2, the proportion of this population who wear glasses for reading

Conclusions:
- what are the populations from which the samples are drawn?
- is your choice of subjects likely to have introduced any bias?
- why are these 'approximate' confidence intervals?
- using your confidence intervals, compare the need for glasses for reading in the two different populations

Extensions:
- compare men/women
- calculate an approximate 90% confidence interval for $p_2 - p_1$
- obtain information (perhaps from an optician) on the proportion of these populations who wear glasses for reading. Compare this with your confidence intervals

7.3 Is a foot a foot long?

Requirements:
- 15–20 adult male subjects
- a ruler or other device for measuring feet

Data collection:
- measure one foot of each subject
  (a) with shoes on, x
  (b) with shoes off, y

Analysis:
- calculate a 95% confidence interval for the mean of X, μ_x
- calculate a 95% confidence interval for the mean of Y, μ_y

Conclusions:
- what is the population from which the sample is drawn?
- is your choice of subjects likely to have introduced any bias?
- what assumption(s) have you made about the distribution of foot lengths?
- does your confidence interval for μ_x contain the measurement 1 foot (30.5 cm)?
- does your confidence interval for μ_y contain the measurement 1 foot?
- based on your results: is a foot a foot long?

Extensions:
- repeat the exercise for adult females
- calculate confidence intervals for the difference in mean foot length for adult males and females
- for each individual, calculate the difference in foot length and shoe length. Calculate a confidence interval for the difference
- calculate confidence intervals for the standard deviations

7.4 Random Normal variables I

The analysis of data in this exercise is repetitive and is best done using a computer program. For this reason the format of the exercise has been altered.

Requirements:
- computer program to generate random Normal variables or the data set provided in Table 1 in the Appendix, p. 132

Section A

Data collection and analysis:
- use the computer program to generate 6 observations from the distribution $X \sim N(20, 4^2)$
- calculate $\bar{x}$, the mean of this sample
- calculate a 60% confidence interval for μ, the population mean, using $\sigma = 4$
- repeat for 100 samples

Conclusions:
- what proportion of your intervals contain μ (=20)?
- is this observed proportion consistent with the percentage confidence of your interval?

Section B

- repeat Section A using sample size 6 and a 90% confidence interval

Section C

- repeat Section A using sample size 20 and a 60% confidence interval

Section D

- repeat Section A using sample size 20 and a 90% confidence interval

General conclusions:
- how does the percentage confidence affect the width of the interval?
- how does the sample size affect the width of the interval?

Extensions:
- using the same data and confidence percentages, calculate confidence intervals for the standard deviation and carry out the same analysis

7.5 Random Normal variables II

The analysis of data in this exercise is repetitive and is best done using a computer program. For this reason the format of the exercise has been altered.

Requirements:
- computer program to generate random Normal variables or the data set provided in Table 1 in the Appendix, p. 132

Section A

Data collection and analysis:
- use the computer program to generate 3 observations from the distribution $X \sim N(20, 4^2)$
- calculate $\bar{x}$, the mean of this sample
- calculate $\hat{\sigma}^2 = \dfrac{\Sigma(x - \bar{x})^2}{n - 1}$, the best estimate of σ^2
- calculate an 80% confidence interval for μ, the population mean, using the t-distribution and $\hat{\sigma}^2$
- repeat this analysis for 100 samples of size 3
- for each sample of size 3 which you have generated, calculate also an interval
  $$\bar{x} \pm 1.2816 \frac{\hat{\sigma}}{\sqrt{n}}$$ (i.e. use the corresponding z value instead of the t value)

Conclusions:
- what proportion of the intervals based on t contain μ, the population mean?
- what proportion of the intervals based on z contain μ?
- which of the two methods, t or z, yields more reliable confidence intervals for samples of size 3?

Section B

Data collection and analysis:
- repeat Section A for samples of size 20

Conclusions:
- which of the two methods, t or z, yields more reliable confidence intervals for samples of size 20?

General conclusions:
- when calculating a confidence interval for a mean, standard deviation unknown, how important is it to use a t value rather than a z value?

- how is your answer affected by the sample size?

Hypothesis testing

Notes for students

An hypothesis test is used to decide, on the basis of a sample, whether to accept or to reject a claim about a population parameter. The calculations for hypothesis testing are basically the same as those for confidence intervals, but the purpose is different.

Definitions

- **Null hypothesis** H_0 defines the claim to be tested by specifying a distribution and the necessary parameters. It must contain an equals sign.
- **Alternative hypothesis** H_1 defines any alternative to H_0 and can be used to distinguish between one-tailed and two-tailed tests.
- **Type I error** – rejecting a true null hypothesis. The risk of making a type I error is often called the significance level of the test.
- **Type II error** – accepting a false null hypothesis.

For any given test, reducing the risk of type I error will increase the risk of type II error and vice versa. For a given risk of type I error, the risk of type II error may be reduced by increasing the sample size.

Tests on discrete distributions

- **Binomial** – test for p. Use the exact test for small samples and the Normal approximation for large samples.
- **Poisson** – test for mean. Use the exact test for small means and the Normal approximation for large means.

Tests which assume Normal distribution

Let $x_1, x_2, \ldots, x_n$ be a random sample from $X \sim N(\mu_x, \sigma_x^2)$ and

let $y_1, y_2, \ldots, y_m$ be a random sample from $Y \sim N(\mu_y, \sigma_y^2)$.

Test		Statistic		Critical value from
$\mu_x = \mu$	σ_x known	$\dfrac{\bar{x} - \mu}{\sigma_x/\sqrt{n}}$		z
$\mu_x = \mu$	σ_x not known	$\dfrac{\bar{x} - \mu}{\hat{\sigma}_x/\sqrt{n}}$		t_{n-1}
$\mu_x = \mu_y$	σ_x, σ_y known	$\dfrac{\bar{x} - \bar{y}}{\sqrt{\sigma_x^2/n + \sigma_y^2/m}}$		z
$\mu_x = \mu_y$	$\sigma_x = \sigma_y$ but unknown	$\dfrac{\bar{x} - \bar{y}}{\hat{\sigma}\sqrt{1/n + 1/m}}$	$\hat{\sigma}^2 = \dfrac{(n-1)\hat{\sigma}_x^2 + (m-1)\hat{\sigma}_y^2}{n + m - 2}$	t_{n+m-2}
$\sigma_x = \sigma_y$		$\hat{\sigma}_x^2 / \hat{\sigma}_y^2$		$F_{n-1,\, m-1}$
$\sigma_x = \sigma$	μ_x known	$\dfrac{\Sigma(x - \mu_x)^2}{\sigma^2}$		χ_n^2
$\sigma_x = \sigma$	μ_x not known	$\dfrac{\Sigma(x - \bar{x})^2}{\sigma^2}$		χ_{n-1}^2

8.1 Vital statistics

This exercise has been written for blood pressure data but it can be used for other medical data where the population mean and standard deviation figures are published. Students may wish to use the following blood pressure figures, in (mm Hg) for a population aged between 31 and 62:

Diastolic $\mu = 84.8$ and $\sigma = 12.8$

Systolic $\mu = 135.8$ and $\sigma = 22.3$

Requirements:
- a device for testing blood pressure
- 20 subjects drawn from a suitable stratum of the population (suitable in the sense that the population mean and standard deviation figures are available)

Data collection:
- measure the blood pressures of each of the subjects

Analysis:
- calculate the mean, $\bar{x}$, of your sample
- assuming that the standard deviation, σ, given in the published data is correct, test the hypothesis that your sample comes from a population with the published mean

Conclusions:
- what is the population from which the sample is drawn?
- is your choice of subjects likely to have introduced any bias?
- is it reasonable to assume that the published standard deviation is correct?
- is it reasonable to assume that X is normally distributed?
- do your calculations support the hypothesis about the mean?

Extensions:
- repeat the test on the mean using a t-test
- use χ^2 to test whether your sample could have come from the population with the published standard deviation

8.2 Kids

The Office of Population Censuses and Surveys projects that 20% of women born in the last 30 years will remain childless.   [*The Guardian*, 11 April 95]

Requirements:	• 20 subjects from the population of female A-level students (or other appropriate group)
Data collection:	• ask each subject 'Do you intend to remain childless?' • record the number who say 'yes', x
Analysis:	• test the hypothesis that p, the proportion of female A-level students who intend to remain childless, is 0.20
Conclusions:	• what is the population from which your sample was drawn? • is your choice of subjects likely to have biased the result? • are the intentions expressed by your sample consistent with the projection in the published article?
Extensions:	• take a larger sample and test using a Normal approximation • collect data from other groups of women born in the last 30 years and compare • collect data from boys born in the last 30 years and compare

8.3 Letters

Requirements:
- data collection sheet

Data collection:
- define a 'letter' as opposed to junk mail, advertisements, etc.
- count the number of letters, x, received by a household on each of 30 days
- count the number of letters, y, received by a friend's household on each of 10 days. Record this data in the order in which it is collected

Analysis:
- gather the X data into a frequency distribution where f is the number of days (out of 30)

x	0	1	2	...
Observed f				

- calculate $\bar{x}$ and s_x^2
- calculate the distribution of expected frequencies based on $X \sim Po(\bar{x})$
- draw bar line diagrams of the expected frequencies and the observed frequencies either aligned one below the other or on the same axes
- assume that Y follows a Poisson distribution and assume also that $\mu_x = \bar{x}$ (this is not to be encouraged but it is necessary for this exercise)
- using y_1, the number of letters on the first day, test the hypothesis $\mu_y = \mu_x$
- using $y_1 + y_2$, the total number of letters on the first 2 days, test the hypothesis $\mu_y = \mu_x$ (*Note:* to do this test whether $y_1 + y_2$ could be an observation from $Po(2\mu_x)$)
- using Σy_i, the total number of letters in 10 days, test the hypothesis $\mu_y = \mu_x$ using the Normal approximation

Conclusions:
- what is the population from which each sample is drawn?
- is your method of sampling likely to have introduced any bias?
- does the Poisson distribution provide an adequate model for the distribution of X?
- based on your conclusion about the distribution of X, is the assumption that Y follows a Poisson distribution a reasonable one?
- discuss the assumption that $\mu_x = \bar{x}$
- what do the tests indicate about the mean of the distribution of your friend's post?
- if your friend's mean is different from yours, are you more likely to detect the difference using 10 days' data or one day's data?

Extensions:
- test for goodness of fit

8.4 Puzzles

Requirements:
- 2 simple puzzles – one word and one number
- a watch for timing in seconds
- 10 subjects

Data collection:
- do a pilot study to select two puzzles of a similar level of difficulty which will each take between 1 and 2 minutes to solve
- ask the subjects to do puzzle A and puzzle B, timing each. Alternate the order of presentation

Analysis:
- for each subject, calculate $d = $ time(A) – time(B)
- use the *t*-test to test the hypothesis that the mean difference in the time taken to do the puzzles is zero

Conclusions:
- what is the population from which the sample is drawn?
- is your choice of subjects likely to have introduced any bias?
- is there any reason to suspect that the d values do not form a Normal distribution?
- is there a significant difference between the times to do puzzle A and puzzle B?

Extensions:
- using at least 25 subjects, perform the Wilcoxon signed rank test or the Sign test
- use the *z*-test to test the difference in times using a sample which is large enough to give a good estimate of the population standard deviation
- let some subjects do puzzle A and other subjects do puzzle B and use the unpaired *t*-test to analyse the results (for large samples, the *z*-test can be used)
- use more than two puzzles and test for differences using analysis of variance

8.5 Tower of Hanoi

This exercise is for a Tower of Hanoi puzzle, but it can be carried out using any puzzle or computer simulation.

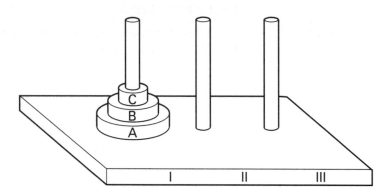

In the Tower of Hanoi puzzle the task is to transfer the discs from one peg to another. One disc is moved at a time. No disc can ever be placed on top of a disc smaller than itself.

Requirements:
- a Tower of Hanoi puzzle or a computer simulation
- about 10 subjects from each of two population groups, for example boys/girls; year 7/year 12; students/parents. The two sets of subjects do not need to be of exactly the same size
- a watch for timing in seconds

Data collection:
- do a pilot study to determine a suitable number of discs so that most subjects will complete the puzzle in less than 2 minutes
- give each subject the instructions and allow a short time for familiarisation
- give the subject the actual puzzle and record the time from start to finish

Analysis:
- use an F-test to test whether the variances of the two samples are equal
- if the variances are equal, use the unpaired t-test to test whether there is a difference in the mean time for the two populations
- if the variances are unequal increase the sample size and use the z-test to test whether there is a difference in the mean time for the two populations

Conclusions:
- what are the populations from which the samples are drawn?
- is your choice of subjects likely to have introduced any bias?
- what assumptions have you made when carrying out the F-test and the t-test?
- do your calculations show a difference between the mean times for the two populations?

Extensions:
- increase the sample size and use the z-test
- using more than two groups and/or more than one puzzle, test for differences using analysis of variance

8.6 Random Normal variables III

The analysis of data in this exercise is repetitive and best done using a computer program. For this reason the format of the exercise has been altered.

Requirements:
- a computer program to generate random Normal variables, or data from Table 1 in the Appendix, p. 132

Section A

Data collection:
- use a computer to generate 6 observations from the distribution $X \sim N(20, 4^2)$
- repeat 100 times to give 100 samples each of size 6

Analysis:
- calculate $\bar{x}$ for each sample
- for each sample, test the hypothesis
    $H_0: \mu = 20$
    $H_1: \mu \neq 20$
  (assume that $\sigma = 4$) at the *(a)* 5% and *(b)* 20% significance level
- record the number of times that H_0 is rejected at *(a)* 5% and also at *(b)* 20% significance level

Conclusions:
- are the results of the hypothesis testing consistent with the relevant significance levels?
- explain what is meant by type I and type II error in the context of this exercise
- is it possible to make a type II error when testing $\mu = 20$?

Section B

Data collection:
- repeat Section A with a sample size of 20

Analysis:
- as for Section A

Conclusions:
- what is the effect on type I error when the sample size is increased?

Section C

Data collection:
- use the same data as in Section A

Analysis:
- for each sample, test the hypothesis
    $H_0: \mu = 18$
    $H_1: \mu \neq 18$
  (assume that $\sigma = 4$) at the *(a)* 5% and *(b)* 20% significance level
- record the number of times that H_0 is rejected at *(a)* 5% and also at *(b)* 20% significance level

Conclusions:
- explain what is meant by a type II error in the context of this exercise
- is it possible to make a type I error when testing that $\mu = 18$?
- how is the risk of type I error related to the risk of type II error?

Section D

Data collection:
- use the data from Section B

Analysis:
- for each sample, test the hypothesis
$$H_0: \mu = 18$$
$$H_1: \mu \neq 18$$
as in Section C

Final conclusions:
- do these results confirm your earlier conclusions about the relationship between the risk of type I and the risk of type II error?
- how is the risk of type II error affected by the increase in the sample size?

Extensions:
- repeat Sections A and B testing $\sigma = 4$ using the χ^2 test
- repeat Sections C and D testing $\sigma = 5$ using the χ^2 test
- repeat Sections C and D testing $\mu = 17$
- investigate one-sided tests
- repeat the entire exercise using the t-test

8.7 Weighing

Requirements:
- a standard weight (unmarked)
- a calibrated weighing machine
- 10–15 subjects

Data collection:
- conduct a pilot study to determine the accuracy to which the weight should be measured. The degree of accuracy must be such that there will be some variability in the results obtained
- ask each subject to weigh the weight and record the result to the determined accuracy

Analysis:
- carry out a *t*-test to test whether the mean of the population of recorded weights is equal to the actual weight of the object

Conclusions:
- what is the population from which the sample is drawn?
- is your choice of subjects likely to have introduced any bias?
- what assumptions have you made when carrying out the *t*-test?
- is there a significant difference between the mean recorded value and the actual weight of the object?
- comment on the variability of the recorded weights

Extensions:
- calculate confidence intervals for the mean and standard deviation of the recorded weights
- compare different groups of subjects, for example male/female; science students/arts students
- ask each subject to do several weighings using same/different weights on same/different scales. Test for differences using analysis of variance

8.8 Precision of measurements

This exercise has been written for measuring length. It could equally well be used for comparing the precision of any two comparable pieces of measuring equipment.

Requirements:
- tape measure (in cm)
- good quality ruler (about 20 cm long)
- about 20 subjects

Data collection:
- draw neatly, in ink, a straight line approximately 12 cm long
- ask about 10 subjects to measure the line to the nearest 0.1 mm, using the ruler. Record the measurements
- ask the rest of the subjects to measure the line to the nearest 0.1 mm using the tape measure. Record the measurements.
  (The two groups do not need to be of the same size)

Analysis:
- carry out an *F*-test to test whether the samples come from populations with equal variances

Conclusions:
- what is the population from which the samples are drawn?
- is your choice of subjects likely to have introduced any bias?
- what assumptions have you made when carrying out the *F*-test?
- discuss the difference, if any, in the two measuring devices, noting which gives more precision
- discuss other statistics important in deciding the effectiveness of a measuring device

Extensions:
- compare the two samples using the Mann Whitney *U* test
- if you know the exact length of the line, test whether each sample could come from a population with this mean
- collect paired measurements and use the Sign test, Wilcoxon's signed rank test or a paired *t*-test to compare the measuring devices

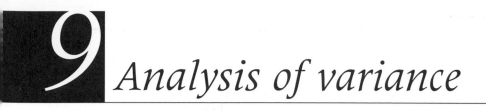

Analysis of variance

Notes for students

One-factor analysis of variance

Factor level	Performance	Total
G_1	$x_{11} \ldots x_{1m}$	T_1
G_2	$x_{21} \ldots x_{2m}$	T_2
$\vdots$	$\vdots$	$\vdots$
G_n	$x_{n1} \ldots x_{nm}$	T_n

Grand total $= T$

Model

$$x_{ij} = \mu + G_i + \varepsilon_{ij}$$

where μ is the overall mean

G_i is the effect of the ith level of G ($\mu_G = 0$)

$\varepsilon_{ij} \sim N(0, \sigma^2)$ is experimental error

Suppose x_{ij} is the yield of a particular crop when a particular type of fertiliser, G_i, is used. Then x_{ij} is affected by many factors, for example weather and soil fertility, as well as by G_i. The combined effect of all these other factors is called **experimental error**.

The model assumes:

1. $\varepsilon_{ij} \sim N(0, \sigma^2)$ is Normally distributed and independent of the particular type of fertiliser used, and

2. x_{ij} is the result of **adding** the overall mean, the effect of the ith type of fertiliser and the experimental error.

The assumptions are reasonable in many applications. They can never be proved to be true but it is good practice to check that they are plausible.

Analysis of variance table

Source of variability	Degrees of freedom (DF)	Sum of squares (SS)	Mean square (MS)
Between G's	$n - 1$	$\sum \left(\dfrac{T_i^2}{m} \right) - \dfrac{T^2}{mn}$	SS/DF
Residual	$n(m - 1)$	$\sum x_{ij}^2 - \sum \left(\dfrac{T_i^2}{m} \right)$	SS/DF
Total	$mn - 1$	$\sum x_{ij}^2 - \dfrac{T^2}{mn}$	

Note 1: Residual SS = total SS − between G's SS, and is usually calculated in this way.

Note 2: If samples are of unequal size replace mn by $\sum m_i$ and m by m_i.

To test H_0: no difference between G's,

calculate $\dfrac{\text{between } G\text{'s MS}}{\text{residual MS}}$ and compare with critical value from $F_{(n-1), n(m-1)}$.

Two-factor analysis of variance

	J_1	J_2	$\cdots$	J_m	Total
G_1	x_{11}	x_{12}	$\cdots$	x_{1m}	$T_{1\bullet}$
G_2	x_{21}	x_{22}	$\cdots$	x_{2m}	$T_{2\bullet}$
$\vdots$	$\vdots$	$\vdots$	$\vdots$	$\vdots$	$\vdots$
G_n	x_{n1}	x_{n2}	$\cdots$	x_{nm}	$T_{n\bullet}$
Total	$T_{\bullet 1}$	$T_{\bullet 2}$	$\cdots$	$T_{\bullet m}$	Grand total $T_{\bullet\bullet}$

Model

$$x_{ij} = \mu + G_i + F_j + \varepsilon_{ij}$$

where μ is the overall mean

G_i is the effect of the ith level of $G(\mu_G = 0)$

F_j is the effect of the jth level of $F(\mu_F = 0)$

$\varepsilon_{ij} \sim N(0, \sigma^2)$ is experimental error

The assumptions are the same as for the one-factor model with one important addition: that there is no interaction between G and F.

Suppose that x_{ij} is the crop yield, G_i is the type of fertiliser and F_j is the interval between watering. Then the model assumes that the effect of G_i is the same whatever the interval between watering. It would not be valid if one type of fertiliser was effective if used in combination with frequent watering but ineffective without frequent watering. Interactions can be investigated but are beyond the scope of these exercises.

Analysis of variance table

Source of variability	Degrees of freedom (DF)	Sum of squares (SS)	Mean square (MS)
Between G's	$n - 1$	$\sum \dfrac{T_{i\bullet}^2}{m} - \dfrac{T_{\bullet\bullet}^2}{mn}$	SS/DF
Between F's	$m - 1$	$\sum \dfrac{T_{\bullet j}^2}{n} - \dfrac{T_{\bullet\bullet}^2}{mn}$	SS/DF
Residual	$(n - 1)(m - 1)$	$\sum x_{ij}^2 - \sum \dfrac{T_{i\bullet}^2}{m} - \sum \dfrac{T_{\bullet j}^2}{n} + \dfrac{T_{\bullet\bullet}^2}{mn}$	SS/DF
Total	$mn - 1$	$\sum x_{ij}^2 - \sum \dfrac{T_{\bullet\bullet}^2}{mn}$	

Note: Residual SS = total SS – between G's SS – between F's SS

To test H_0: no difference between G's

calculate $\dfrac{\text{between } G\text{'s MS}}{\text{residual MS}}$ and compare with critical value from $F_{(n-1),\,(n-1)(m-1)}$

To test H_0: no difference between F's

calculate $\dfrac{\text{between } F\text{'s MS}}{\text{residual MS}}$ and compare with critical value from $F_{(m-1),\,(n-1)(m-1)}$

9.1 Jigsaws

Requirements:
- four home-made cardboard jigsaw puzzles, with about 6–8 pieces each. The pieces of each puzzle should be identical shapes to the pieces in the other puzzles.
  - A: covered in plain white paper
  - B: covered in a small repeating pattern
  - C: covered in a line drawing
  - D: covered in a simple coloured picture

  Commercially available children's jigsaws can be used if suitable
- a watch for timing seconds
- about 20 subjects

Data collection:
- decide on standard conditions under which puzzles are to be done. Consider for example, show/not show pictures first, puzzle pieces mixed and right side up, etc.
- allocate approximately one quarter of the subjects to each jigsaw by a random method
- record puzzle type and time to complete for each subject

Analysis:
- carry out a one-factor analysis of variance on the results, testing for differences between puzzles
- calculate a mean time for each puzzle
- calculate a standard deviation for each puzzle

Conclusions:
- what is the population from which the sample is drawn?
- is your choice of subjects likely to have introduced any bias?
- is the allocation of subjects likely to have introduced any bias?
- is the model plausible in the light of the standard deviations?
- is there a significant difference between mean completion times for each puzzle?
- what, if any, order of difficulty is suggested by the mean times for completion?
- consider the advantages/disadvantages of having each subject do all four puzzles

Extensions:
- examine your data considering whether a multiplicative model might be more suitable than the additive model. Apply the analysis to log(times)
- introduce further factor(s) such as age of subjects, with/without music playing, etc.

9.2 Above/below

Students will have to write their own program (described in Data collection).
A similar exercise may be carried out using flash cards.

Requirements:
- a computer using the appropriate program
- 10–15 subjects

Data collection:
- the computer presents subjects with a horizontal line accompanied by the word ABOVE or BELOW written either above or below the line. The subject presses B on the keyboard if the word is below the line and A if it is above the line. They respond to the location and not to the word
- before beginning the test instruct the subject that it is important to give the correct answer as well as to respond as quickly as possible to the stimulus. Give each subject a short practice session
- give each subject 3 sets of stimuli, each set with 20 screens as follows:
  - *(i)* with 20% false screens (for example, the word ABOVE printed below the line and vice versa)
  - *(ii)* with 50% false screens   *(iii)* with 80% false screens

  The order of presentation of the sets should be random for each subject
- the program records for each subject
  - *(a)* the number of errors   *(b)* the mean response time for each set
- discard all of the data for any subject who makes more than three errors on any set

Analysis:
- gather the mean response times into a table

Person/set	i	ii	iii
1			
2			
.			

- carry out a two-factor analysis of variance and test for differences between sets and for differences between subjects
- calculate the overall mean for each set
- find the median and quartiles of mean times for each set
- draw box and whisker diagrams for each set

Conclusions:
- what is the population from which the sample is drawn?
- is your choice of subjects likely to have introduced any bias?
- is there a significant difference between sets?
- is there a significant difference between subjects?
- what do the box and whisker diagrams suggest about a possible relationship between response time and the proportion of false stimuli?

Extensions:
- include more values of percentage of false screens and examine the results using regression analysis
- compare different groups of subjects, (male/female, etc.)

9.3 Sorting

Requirements:
- 13 playing cards – a single suit from a full pack
- a watch for timing in seconds
- about 5 subjects

Data collection:
- ask each subject to arrange the cards in order. You will need to explain to each subject what 'in order' means (do not allow a practice) and also to decide on the conditions for the test – presentation, etc.
- shuffle the cards, give them to the subject and record the time taken to sort the cards
- shuffle and repeat 3 more times
- repeat this entire process for each subject

Analysis:
- gather the results into a table

Subject

Sort	A	B	C	D	E
1					
2					
3					
4					

- carry out a two-factor analysis of variance and test for differences between the sorts and for differences between the subjects
- calculate the mean time for each sort

Conclusions:
- what is the population from which the sample is drawn?
- is your choice of subjects likely to have introduced any bias?
- is there a significant difference between subjects?
- is there a significant difference between sorts?
- is there evidence of a learning effect?

Extensions:
- use 13 cards, each displaying a randomly chosen letter of the alphabet
- compare different populations, for example card players/non card players; different ages, etc.
- examine the effect of environment. For example, repeat the exercise in a quiet room, in front of the TV, in the common room, etc.

9.4 Volume

Requirements:
- a scale, a ruler and a calibrated container of water
- a rectilinear, spherical or cylindrical solid object of known density (which will not float)
- instructions for calculating volume by each of the three methods (as in Data collection)
- about 25 subjects

Data collection:
- divide the subjects randomly into three groups of similar, but not necessarily equal size
- ask each member of group A to calculate the volume of the object by immersing it in the water
- ask each member of group B to calculate the volume of the object by measuring the dimensions and substituting in the appropriate equation
- ask each member of group C to calculate the volume of the object by weighing it and dividing by the density

Analysis:
- carry out a one-factor analysis of variance on the results, testing for differences between methods
- if you have enough data, draw box and whisker diagrams for each method, on the same page for comparison
- calculate a mean and a standard deviation for each method

Conclusions:
- what is the population from which the sample is drawn?
- are your choice and/or allocations of subjects likely to have introduced any bias?
- is there a significant difference between the methods of calculating volume?
- examine the mean volume and/or the diagrams for each method.
  (a) If the volume is known, comment on the relative accuracy
  (b) If the volume is not known, comment on the differences between the means
- examine the standard deviations and/or diagrams and compare the variability of the methods. Is this consistent with the analysis of variance assumption that the variance of each method is the same?
- how did/would you deal with the results of subjects who carried out the method incorrectly and got wildly incorrect answers?

Extensions:
- have each subject do all three methods and carry out two-factor analysis of variance
- is variability less amongst science students than among arts students?

10 Bivariate data

Notes for students

In these exercises on correlation and regression we have tried to draw attention to the statistical difference between these two models, while not denying that in some situations it is sensible to use both techniques on the same set of data.

Product–moment correlation coefficient, ρ

This is a measure of the strength of the *linear* relationship between two independent random variables X and Y where $-1 \leqslant \rho \leqslant +1$. For observed variables (x_i, y_i) ρ is estimated by

$$r = \frac{\Sigma\,(x_i - \bar{x})(y_i - \bar{y})}{\sqrt{\Sigma\,(x_i - \bar{x})^2\,\Sigma\,(y_i - \bar{y})^2}}$$

There are many alternative versions of this equation. r is most easily found directly from your calculator. Tables for testing $H_o: \rho = 0$ assume that X and Y follow a bivariate Normal distribution. Where this is not the case, some strange results can occur. For example:

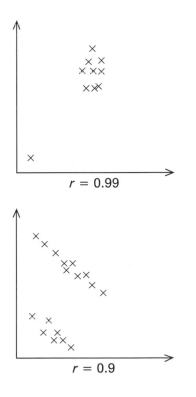

$r = 0.99$

$r = 0.9$

Rank correlation coefficients

These require less calculation than the product–moment correlation coefficient. This is no longer relevant since we have computers to do the calculations, but they are still used for certain non-linear relationships. The most common, Spearman's rank correlation coefficient, is in fact the product–moment correlation coefficient calculated on ranked data. Provided that there are no tied ranks

$$r_S = 1 - \frac{6\Sigma d_i^2}{n(n^2 - 1)} \qquad d_i = x_i - y_i$$

where x_i and y_i are ranks

Regression

Unlike correlation, where the two variables are interchangeable, in regression the response variable Y clearly depends on the explanatory variable X where $Y = \alpha + \beta X + \varepsilon$ where $\varepsilon \sim N(0, \sigma^2)$ and X may be set to any required value. In practice, it is often useful to apply the regression model even when the conditions are not completely met.

For n pairs of observed variables (x_i, v_i), β is estimated by

$$b = \frac{\Sigma\,(x_i - \bar{x})\,(y_i - \bar{y})}{\sqrt{\Sigma\,(x_i - \bar{x})^2}}$$

and α by

$$a = \bar{y} - b\bar{x}$$

a and b are most easily found directly from your calculator.

Residuals

A residual is the difference between the observed value of y and the corresponding value predicted by the model. For the observed (x_i, y_i) it is estimated by

$$y_i - (a + bx_i)$$

In some of the regression exercises students are asked to calculate the average magnitude of the residuals. For mathematical reasons this is often estimated by

$$\sqrt{\frac{\Sigma(y_i - a - bx_i)^2}{n-2}}$$

However, it may make more sense to students to estimate it by

$$\frac{\Sigma|y_i - a - bx_i|}{n}$$

and this is perfectly acceptable.

One advantage of the first method is that it may be calculated by using the formula

$$\Sigma(y_i - a - bx_i)^2 = \Sigma y_i^2 - a\Sigma y_i - b\Sigma x_i y_i$$

thus avoiding the necessity of calculating each residual individually.

10.1 **Clothes**

Requirements:
- 12 pictures of items of clothing
- the prices should be known, but not to the subject, and should vary fairly evenly over a wide range
- 1 subject

Data collection:
- display pictures (without price) to the subject. Instruct subject to arrange them in price order

Analysis:
- calculate a rank correlation coefficient between the actual price order and the subject's order
- test whether the rank correlation coefficient differs from zero

Conclusions:
- what is the population from which the items of clothing have been chosen?
- is your choice of items of clothing likely to have introduced any bias?
- is your choice of subject likely to have introduced any bias?
- is there evidence of agreement between the subject's ranking and the actual ranking?

Extensions:
- repeat the exercise for a second subject and find the rank correlation coefficient between the two subjects. Test this rank correlation coefficient
- do girls' rankings correlate better with the actual ranks than boys'? Compare different ages, boys' clothes/girls' clothes, etc.

10.2 Estimating age I

Requirements:
- 15 photographs of people, with the person's age known at the time when the photograph was taken. The ages should vary fairly evenly from about 2 to 80 years old
- 1 subject

Data collection:
- decide, possibly by conducting a pilot study, whether age is to be recorded to the nearest year, or otherwise
- arrange the photographs in a random order
- show the first photograph to the subject, who should estimate the age of the person shown
- remove the photograph
- repeat for the remaining photos, recording the actual age, x, and the estimated age, y, for each

Analysis:
- draw a scatter diagram
- examine the scatter diagram and, if suitable, calculate the equation of the regression line of y on x
- draw the regression line on the scatter diagram
- show, on your graph, the residual for each point

Conclusions:
- what is the population from which your photographs were drawn?
- is your choice of photographs likely to have affected your result?
- is your choice of subject likely to have introduced any bias?
- why was the regression of y on x calculated rather than x on y?
- is the relationship between y and x approximately linear?
- is there any pattern displayed by the residuals? For example, do they tend to increase/decrease with x? Do they tend to differ in magnitude or sign with the sex of the person photographed?
- compare your calculated regression line with the line $y = x$
- what does your diagram suggest about your subject's ability to estimate age?

Extensions:
- calculate the average magnitude of the residuals
- calculate the product–moment correlation coefficient between x and y
  Note: as y clearly depends on x in this exercise, regression is the appropriate model. However, the correlation coefficient may still be calculated as a measure of the strength of the relationship between y and x (assuming this relationship is linear)
- repeat this exercise with a second subject. Compare the average magnitude of the residuals of the two subjects

10.3 **Germinating peas**

Requirements:
- 30–50 peas for germination
- seed tray(s) and compost or wet paper

Data collection:
- you may wish to do a pilot study. Germinate a few peas in order to decide how and to what accuracy measurements should be made
- space peas evenly in the tray and moisten. Put the tray in a suitable place for germination
- when about 30 peas have germinated remove them carefully and measure the length of the green shoot, x, and the length of the root, y

Analysis:
- draw a scatter diagram
- calculate the product-moment correlation coefficient between x and y
- test whether the product-moment correlation coefficient differs from zero

Conclusions:
- is the product-moment correlation coefficient consistent with the pattern displayed in the scatter diagram?

Extensions:
- calculate the regression line of y on x and use it to predict the average root length for a shoot of length 2 cm
  Note: as y and x are associated in this exercise, but neither is clearly the explanatory variable, correlation is the appropriate model. However, regression may be used – with caution – in order to make predictions
- calculate the regression line of x on y and use it to predict the average shoot length for a root of length 3 cm

10.4 Pulse rate in exercise

Requirements:
- a step for step-ups
- a watch to measure pulse rate
- 1 subject

Data collection:
- a trial consists of the subject doing x step-ups after which the pulse rate, y, is recorded. There should be 10 trials altogether corresponding to 2,4,6, . . . , 20 step-ups. The trials are to be carried out in random order and the subject is to rest between trials to allow the pulse rate to return to normal. The trials can be carried out on separate days if preferred

Analysis:
- plot a scatter diagram of the data
- if suitable, calculate and draw the regression line of y on x

Conclusions:
- is your choice of subject likely to have introduced any bias?
- why is the number of step-ups the explanatory variable in this exercise?
- do the points indicate a linear relationship between y and x?
- if you have fitted a regression line $y = a + bx$, interpret a and b in the context of the exercise
- suggest a range of numbers of step-ups within which a reasonably accurate estimate of the pulse rate might be made based on your calculations

Extensions:
- predict the pulse rates for two values of x, one within the suggested range and one well outside this range. Test your predictions experimentally
- calculate the product–moment correlation coefficient between x and y and test the hypothesis that $\rho = 0$
  Note: as y clearly depends on x in this exercise, regression is the appropriate model. However, the correlation coefficient may still be calculated as a measure of the strength of the relationship between y and x (assuming this relationship is linear)
- repeat the experiment for contrasting subjects, for example, male/female; younger/older; fit/unfit; heavy/slim

10.5 Estimating age II

Requirements:
- 15 photographs of people, with the person's age known at the time when the photograph was taken. The ages should vary fairly evenly from about 2 to 80 years old
- 9 subjects

Data collection:
- decide, possibly by conducting a pilot study, whether age is to be recorded to the nearest year, or otherwise
- arrange the photographs in a random order
- show the first photograph to the first subject, who should estimate the age of the person shown
- remove the photograph
- repeat for the remaining photos, recording the actual age, x, and the estimated age, y, for each
- repeat for each subject. The order of presentation of the photographs should be different for each subject

Analysis:
- draw a scatter diagram for all of the data (135 data points)
- for each photograph calculate the mean, $\bar{y}$, and standard deviation, s_y, of the estimated age
- draw a scatter diagram of mean estimated age, $\bar{y}$ against actual age, x
- draw a scatter diagram of the standard deviation of the estimated age, s_y against actual age, x
- examine each scatter diagram and, if suitable, calculate and draw the appropriate regression line

Conclusions:
- what is the population from which your photographs were drawn?
- is your choice of photographs likely to have affected your result?
- what is the population from which your subjects were drawn?
- is your choice of subjects likely to have introduced any bias?
- why was x the explanatory rather than the response variable in each case?
- what do you notice about the regression lines in the first two diagrams?
- is there any pattern in the residuals for the $\bar{y}$ on x diagram?
- if you have done Estimating age I, does $\bar{y}$ give a better estimate of x than a single estimate, y?
- do the points in the s_y on x diagram indicate a linear (or any other) relationship?
- what do your diagrams suggest about your subjects' ability to estimate age?

Extensions:
- calculate the average magnitude of the residuals for $\bar{y}$ on x. How does this result compare with that in Estimating age I?
- calculate the product–moment correlation coefficient between x and $\bar{y}$ and also between x and s_y
  Note: as y clearly depends on x in this exercise, regression is the appropriate model. However, the correlation coefficient may still be calculated as a measure of the strength of the relationship between y and x (assuming the relationship is linear)
- repeat the exercise, choosing subjects so that you can compare the estimating abilities of boys and girls or different age groups, etc.

10.6 Tennis player – speed of serve

Requirements:
- a list of data on professional tennis players which includes world ranking, age, sex, height, weight, speed of serve (e.g. *The Official Guide to ATP Tour Player Biographies, Ranking and Statistics*)

Data collection:
- select a random sample of about 40 male tennis players from the list

Analysis:
- plot a scatter diagram of speed of serve, y, against height, h
- if suitable, calculate and draw the regression line of y on h
- calculate the average magnitude of the residuals
- repeat these three steps for
  - *(a)* speed of serve, y, against age, a
  - *(b)* speed of serve, y, against weight, w

Conclusions:
- what is the population from which your sample is drawn?
- is your method of sampling likely to have introduced any bias?
- compare the average residual value for the three explanatory variables
- which of the three explanatory variables appears to be the best predictor of speed of serve?
- for your chosen predictor, suggest a range of values within which reasonably accurate predictions of speed of serve might be made
- could you use any of these equations to predict speeds of serve at a local tennis club?

Extensions:
- repeat this exercise for female tennis players and compare the results to those for the male players
- calculate the product–moment correlation coefficients and test them for significance. Do these support the choice of explanatory variable made earlier?

  Note: as y clearly depends on x in this exercise, regression is the appropriate model. However this correlation coefficient may still be calculated as a measure of the strength of the relationship between x and y (assuming the relationship is linear)
- investigate the relationship between the ranking, y, and speed of serve, x
- repeat this exercise for the top 40 players or (computer power allowing) all ranked players

 The χ^2 test

Notes for students

If a set of observations can be divided into k classes and O_i is the number of observations in class i and E_i is the number expected in that class given an hypothesis H_o, then $\Sigma \dfrac{(O_i - E_i)^2}{E_i}$ is approximately distributed as χ^2 provided that the following conditions hold:

(i) the classes form a sample space, that is, each possible observation will fit into one, and only one, class;

(ii) each O_i is a frequency (not length, percentage, proportion, etc.);

(iii) each E_i is reasonably large, that is, greater than or equal to about 5 (some flexibility is allowed). Pooling of similar classes may be necessary to achieve this. In a contingency table entire rows or entire columns must be combined, not single cells.

Degrees of freedom in all cases are $k - r$ where

k is the number of classes (after pooling) and

r is the number of independent pieces of information derived from the O_i needed to calculate the E_i

	Restrictions	Degrees of freedom
Uniform distribution	totals agree	$k - 1$
Binomial distribution	totals agree, p given	$k - 1$
	totals agree, p estimated	$k - 2$
Poisson distribution	totals agree, μ given	$k - 1$
	totals agree, μ estimated	$k - 2$
Geometric distribution	totals agree, p given	$k - 1$
	totals agree, p estimated	$k - 2$
Exponential distribution	totals agree, λ given	$k - 1$
	totals agree, λ estimated	$k - 2$
Normal distribution	totals agree, μ and σ given	$k - 1$
	totals agree, μ and σ estimated	$k - 3$
Contingency table		(rows $- 1$) (columns $- 1$) if H_o: rows independent of columns

11.1   **School absences**

Requirements: • a class register for one term

Data collection: • omit any weeks which do not include 5 full days at school
   • count the total number of absences which occur at Monday morning registration
   • do the same for the rest of the week days

Analysis: • complete the following table, where E_i is calculated assuming that absences are independent of the day of the week

	Mon	Tues	Wed	Thurs	Fri
Observed frequency O_i					
Expected frequency E_i					

   • test the hypothesis that absences are independent of the day of the week

Conclusions: • what is the population from which your sample is drawn?
   • is your method of sampling likely to have introduced any bias?
   • interpret the result of the hypothesis test
   • if you have rejected the null hypothesis, describe the pattern of absences

Extensions: • repeat the exercise for a different age group or type of school
   • calculate the mean number of absences per week and compare it with data from another time of year
   • absences are sometimes recorded twice each day, am and pm. Repeat the exercise using the following table

	Mon am	Mon pm	Tues am	Tues pm	Wed am	...
O_i						
E_i						

11.2 Digits of π

Requirements:
- the digits of π to 10 000 decimal places (see pages 84–5)

Data collection:
- use a calculator to generate one random digit
- starting from the first occurrence of that digit, count x_1, all digits up to and including the second occurrence of that digit. Record x_1
- starting from the second occurrence of that digit, count x_2, all digits up to and including the third occurrence of that digit. Record x_2
- continue until about 60 observations have been collected

Analysis:
- gather the observed data into a frequency distribution

x	0	1	2	...
Observed f				

- use a χ^2 approximation to test whether a Geometric distribution with parameter 0.1 is a suitable model for this data
- using the data, calculate p_s, the proportion of the chosen digit in your sample
- use a χ^2 approximation to test whether the Geometric distribution with parameter p_s is a suitable model for this data

Conclusions:
- is your selection of a starting digit likely to have introduced any bias?
- is the data consistent with the hypothesis that your digit occurs randomly with $p = 0.1$?
- is the data consistent with the hypothesis that your digit occurs randomly with $p = p_s$?

Extensions:
- repeat for e or other irrational numbers
- repeat for π using other digits

The first 10 000 decimal places of π

PI = 3.+

1415926535	8979323846	2643383279	5028841971	6939937510	5820974944	5923078164	0628620899	8628034825	3421170679
8214808651	3282306647	0938446095	5058223172	5359408128	4811174502	8410270193	8521105559	6446229489	5493038196
4428810975	6659334461	2847564823	3786783165	2712019091	4564856692	3460348610	4543266482	1339360726	0249141273
7245870066	0631558817	4881520920	9628292540	9171536436	7892590360	0113305305	4882046652	1384146951	9415116094
3305727036	5759591953	0921861173	8193261179	3105118548	0744623799	6274956735	1885752724	8912279381	8301194912
9833673362	4406566430	8602139494	6395224737	1907021798	6094370277	0539217176	2931767523	8467481846	7669405132
0005681271	4526356082	7785771342	7577896091	7363717872	1468440901	2249534301	4654958537	1050792279	6892589235
4201995611	2129021960	8640344181	5981362977	4771309960	5187072113	4999999837	2978049951	0597317328	1609631859
5024459455	3469083026	4252230825	3344685035	2619311881	7101000313	7838752886	5875332083	8142061717	7669147303
5982534904	2875546873	1159562863	8823537875	9375195778	1857780532	1712268066	1300192787	6611195909	2164201989

3809525720	1065485863	2788659361	5338182796	8230301952	0353018529	6899577362	2599413891	2497217752	8347913151
5574857242	4541506959	5082953311	6861727855	8890750983	8175463746	4939319255	0604009277	0167113900	9848824012
8583616035	6370766010	4710181942	9555961989	4676783744	9448255379	7747268471	0404753464	6208046684	2590694912
9331367702	8989152104	7521620569	6602405803	8150193511	2533824300	3558764024	7496473263	9141992726	0426992279
6782354781	6360093417	2164121992	4586315030	2861829745	5570674983	8505494588	5869269956	9092721079	7509302955
3211653449	8720275596	0236480665	4991198818	3479775356	6369807426	5425278625	5181841757	4672890977	7727938000
8164706001	6145249192	1732172147	7235014144	1973568548	1613611573	5255213347	5741849468	4385233239	0739414333
4547762416	8625189835	6948556209	9219222184	2725502542	5688767179	0494601653	4668049886	2723279178	6085784383
8279679766	8145410095	3883786360	9506800642	2512520511	7392984896	0841284886	2694560424	1965285022	2106611863
0674427862	2039194945	0471237137	8696095636	4371917287	4677646575	7396241389	0865832645	9958133904	7802759009

9465764078	9512694683	9835259570	9825822620	5224894077	2671947826	8482601476	9909026401	3639443745	5305068203
4962524517	4939965143	1429809190	6592509372	2169646151	5709858387	4105978859	5977297549	8930161753	9284681382
6868386894	2774155991	8559252459	5395943104	9972524680	8459872736	4469584865	3836736222	6260991246	0805124388
4390451244	1365497627	8079771569	1435997700	1296160894	4169486855	5848406353	4220722258	2848864815	8456028506
0168427394	5226746767	8895252138	5225499546	6672782398	6456596116	3548862305	7745649803	5593634568	1743241125
1507606947	9451096596	0940252288	7971089314	5669136867	2287489405	6010150330	8617928680	9208747609	1782493858
9009714909	6759852613	6554978189	3129784821	6829989487	2265880485	7564014270	4775551323	7964145152	3746234364
5428584447	9526586782	1051141354	7357395231	1342716610	2135969536	2314429524	8493718711	0145765403	5902799344
0374200731	0578539062	1983874478	0847848968	3321445713	8687519435	0643021845	3191048481	0053706146	8067491927
8191197939	9520614196	6342875444	0643745123	7181921799	9839101591	9561814675	1426912397	4894090718	6494231961

5679452080	9514655022	5231603881	9301420937	6213785595	6638937787	0830390697	9207734672	2182562599	6615014215
0306803844	7734549202	6054146659	2520149744	2850732518	6660021324	3408819071	0486331734	6496514539	0579626856
1005508106	6587969981	6357473638	4052571459	1028970641	4011097120	6280439039	7595156771	5770042033	7869936007
2305587631	7635942187	3125147120	5329281918	2618612586	7321579198	4148488291	6447060957	5270695722	0917567116
7229109816	9091528017	3506712748	5832228718	3520935396	5725121083	5791513698	8209144421	0067510334	6711031412
6711136990	8658516398	3150197016	5151168517	1437657618	3515565088	4909989859	9823873455	2833163550	7647918535
8932261854	8963213293	3089857064	2046752590	7091548141	6549859461	6371802709	8199430992	4488957571	2828905923
2332609729	9712084433	5732654893	8239119325	9746366730	5836041428	1388303203	8249037589	8524374417	0291327656
1809377344	4030707469	2112019130	2033038019	7621101100	4492932151	6084244485	9637669838	9522868478	3123552658
2131449576	8572624334	4189303968	6426243410	7732269780	2807318915	4411010446	8232527162	0105265227	2111660396

6655730925	4711055785	3763466820	6531098965	2691862056	4769312570	5863566201	8558100729	3606598764	8611791045
3348850346	1136576867	5324944166	8039626579	7877185560	8455296541	2665408530	6143444318	5867697514	5661406800
7002378776	5913440171	2749470420	5622305389	9456131407	1127000407	8547332699	3908145466	4645880797	2708266830
6343285878	5698305235	8089330657	5740679545	7163775254	2021149557	6158140025	0126228594	1302164715	5097925923
0990796547	3761255176	5675135751	7829666454	7791745011	2996148903	0463994713	2962107340	4375189573	5961458901
9389713111	7904297828	5647503203	1986915140	2870808599	0480109412	1472213179	4764777262	2414254854	5403321571
8530614228	8137585043	0633217518	2979866223	7172159160	7716692547	4873898665	4949450114	6540628433	6639379003
9769265672	1463853067	3609657120	9180763832	7166416274	8888007869	2560290228	4721040317	2118608204	1900042296
6171196377	9213375751	1495950156	6049631862	9472654736	4252308177	0367515906	7350235072	8354056704	0386743513
6222247715	8915049530	9844489333	0963408780	7693259939	7805419341	4473774418	4263129860	8099888687	4132604721

```
5695162396 5864573021 6315981931 9516735381 2974167729 4786724229 2465436680 0980676928 2382806899 6400482435
4037014163 1496589794 0924323789 6907069779 4223625082 2168895738 3798623001 5937764716 5122893578 6015881617
5578297352 3344604281 5126272037 3431465319 7777416031 9906655418 7639792933 4419521541 3418994854 4473456738
3162499341 9131814809 2777710386 3877343177 2075456545 3220777092 1201905166 0962804909 2636019759 8828161332
3166636528 6193266863 3606273567 6303544775 2803504507 7723554710 5859548702 7908143562 4014517180 6246436267
9456127531 8134078330 3362542327 8394495533 2437205835 3114711199 2606381334 6776879695 9703098339 1307710987
0408591337 4641442822 7726546594 7047458784 7787201927 7152807317 6790817715 7213444730 6057007334 9243693113
8350493163 1284042512 1925651798 0694113523 0131470130 4781643788 5185290928 5452011658 3934196562 1349143415
9562586586 5570552690 4965209858 0338507224 2648293972 8584783163 8887644624 0577775606 8246857926 0395352773
4803048029 0058760758 2510474709 1643961362 6760449256 2742042083 6254543372 2085661190 1315339584 5068772460

2901618766 7952406163 4252257719 5429162991 9306455377 9914037340 4328752628 8896399587 9475729174 6426357455
2540790914 5135711136 9410911939 3251910760 2082520261 8798531887 7058429725 9167781314 9699009019 2116971737
2784768472 6860849003 3770242429 1651300500 5168323364 3503895170 2989392233 4517220138 1280696501 1784408745
1960121228 5993716231 3017114448 4640903890 6449544400 6198690754 8516026327 5052983491 8740786680 8818338510
2283345085 0486082503 9302133219 7155184306 3545500766 8282949304 1377655279 3975175461 3953984683 3936383047
4611996653 8581538420 5685338621 8672523843 2830871123 2827892125 0771262946 3229563989 8989358211 6745627010
2183564622 0134967151 8819097303 8119800497 3407239610 3685406643 1939509790 1906996395 5245300545 0580685501
9567302292 1913933918 5680344903 9820595510 0226353536 1920419947 4553859381 0234395544 9597783779 0237421617
2711172364 3435439478 2218185286 2408514006 6604433258 8856986705 4315470696 5747458550 3323233421 0730154594
0516553790 6866273337 9585511562 5784322988 2737231989 8757141595 7811116358 3300594087 3068121602 8764962867

4460477464 9159950549 7374256269 0104903778 1988635938 1465741268 0492564879 8556145372 3478673303 9046883834
3634655379 4986419270 5638729317 4872332083 7601123029 9113679386 2708943879 9362016295 1541337142 4892830722
0126901475 4668476535 7616477379 4675200490 7571555278 1965362132 3926406160 1363581559 0742220020 3187277605
2772190055 6148425551 8792530343 5139844253 2234157623 3610642506 3904975008 6562710953 5919465897 5141310348
2276930264 7435363256 9160781547 8181152843 6679570611 0861533150 4452124767 9245449454 2368288606 1340841486
3776700961 2071512491 4043027253 8607648236 3414334623 5187577664 5216413767 9690314950 1910857598 4423919862
9164219399 4907236234 6468441173 9403265918 4044378051 3339845257 4239950829 6591228508 5558215725 0310712570
1266830240 2929952220 1187267675 6220415420 5161841634 8475651699 9811614101 0029960783 8690929160 3028840026
9104140792 8862150784 2451670908 7000699282 1206604183 7180653556 7252532567 5328612910 4248776182 5829765157
9594700356 2226293486 0034158722 9805349896 5022629174 8788202734 2092224453 3985626476 6914905562 8425039127

5771028402 7998066365 8254889264 8802545661 0172967026 6407655904 2909945681 5065265305 3718294127 0336931378
5178609040 7086671149 6558343434 7693385781 7113864558 7367812301 4587687126 6034891390 9562009939 3610310291
6161528813 8437909904 2317473363 9480457593 1493140529 7634757481 1935670911 0137751721 0080315590 2485309066
9203767192 2033229094 3346768514 2214477379 3937517034 4366199104 0337531173 5471918550 4644902636 5512816228
8244625759 1633303910 7225383742 1821408835 0865739177 1509682887 4782656995 9957449066 1758344137 5223970968
3408005355 9849175417 3818839994 4697486762 6551658276 5848358845 3142775687 9002909517 0283529716 3445621296
4043523117 6006651012 4120065975 5851276178 5838292041 9748442360 8007193045 7618932349 2292796501 9857187212
7267507981 2554709589 0455635792 1221033346 6974992356 3025494780 2490114195 2123828153 0911407907 3860251522
7429958180 7247162591 5685451333 1239486494 7091?9153 2673430282 4418604142 6363954800 0448002670 4962482017
9289647669 7583183271 3142517029 6923488962 7668440323 2609275249 6035799646 9256504936 8183609003 2380929345

9588970695 3653494060 3402166544 3755890045 6328822505 4525564056 4482465151 8754711962 1844396582 5337543885
6909411303 1509526179 3780029741 2076651479 3942590298 9695946995 5657612186 5619673378 6236256125 2163208628
6922210327 4889218654 3648022967 8070576561 5144632045 9279068212 0738337781 4233562823 6089632080 6822246801
2248261177 1858963814 0918390367 3672220888 3215137555 0037279839 4004152970 0287830766 7094447456 0134556417
2543709069 7939612257 1429894671 5435784687 8861444581 2314593571 9849225284 7160504922 1242470141 2147805734
5510500801 9086996033 0276347870 8108175450 1193071412 2339086639 3833952942 5786905076 4310063835 1983438934
1596131854 3475464955 6978103829 3097164651 4384070070 7360411237 3599834452 2516105070 2705623526 6012764848
3084076118 3013052793 2054274628 6540360367 4532865105 7065874882 2559815793 6789766974 2205750596 8344086973
5020141020 6723585020 0724522653 2651341055 9240150274 2162484391 4035998953 5394590944 0704691209 1409387001
2645600162 3742880210 9276457931 0657922955 2498872758 4610126483 6999892256 9596881592 0560010165 5256375678
```

Facsimile of the first two pages of the computer print-out obtained by Shanks and Wrench, who programmed an IBM 704 to compute π to 100,265 decimal places in July 1961.

11.3 Churches

Requirements:
- a 1 : 50 000 Ordinance Survey map of a rural area (sheet 191 is suitable)

Data collection:
- for each church on the map, record the northing grid reference (including an estimate of tenths). Instructions are given in the key on the map

Analysis:
- arrange northing grid references in ascending order
- record the difference, x, between successive northing grid references
- gather x into a frequency distribution

x	0	1	2	3	...
Observed f					

- use the χ^2 approximation to test whether the exponential distribution is a suitable model for these data

Conclusions:
- what is the population from which the sample is drawn?
- is your method of sampling likely to have introduced bias?
- give reasons why the Exponential distribution was considered to be a possible model for these data
- do your results support the use of this model?
- how would you expect the results to differ if you had used a map of a heavily populated area?

Extensions:
- repeat using eastings
- is the Poisson model suitable for the distribution of churches on this map?

11.4 **Supermarket receipts**

Requirements:
- a local supermarket

Data collection:
- collect about 25 till receipts on one day
- repeat for 2 different days of the week

Analysis:
- record the number of items on each receipt, x
- form a 3×3 contingency table using suitable grouping.
  For example:

		Mon	**Wed**	**Fri**
Items	1 – 10			
	11 – 20			
	> 20			

- use the χ^2 approximation to test whether the number of items per receipt is independent of the day of the week

Conclusions:
- what is the population under investigation?
- is your method of sampling likely to have introduced any bias?
- discuss the result of your test
- discuss any pattern that you have found and factors which may explain it

Extensions:
- investigate different times of day/more days of the week
- compare different supermarkets
- investigate the relationship between the total spent and the number of items purchased
- does the Normal distribution provide a suitable model for the total spent on each receipt?

11.5 Colours

Requirements:
- two identical graded colour charts (these can be obtained from paint shops) containing about 30–40 colours
- a watch for timing seconds
- at least 30 subjects (colour blind subjects are not suitable)
- 5–10 additional subjects for a pilot study

Data collection:

Pilot study
- a pilot study is essential. Ask each subject to choose the best *red*, *blue*, *green* and *yellow* from the colour chart
- select the two colour samples for which these subjects show the greatest agreement. These are the named colours
- ask each of the subjects to choose four colours from the colour chart which they would find difficult or impossible to name
- select the two colours which are most frequently chosen. These are the nameless colours

Main study
- present the subject with the four chosen colours (two named and two nameless) for 5 seconds
- after about 30 seconds present the subject with the full colour chart and ask them to select the four colours
- record which of the four colours were identified correctly
- repeat for all subjects

Analysis:
- draw up a 4 × 2 contingency table showing frequencies

	Colours			
	1	2	3	4
Identified **Not identified**				

- perform a χ^2 test to determine whether correct identification is independent of colour

Conclusions:
- what is the population from which your sample was drawn?
- is your choice of subjects likely to have introduced any bias?
- does your data suggest that the ability to recall colours is independent of the colours offered?
- theory maintains that easily named colours are easier to recall. Does your data support this theory? Comment on your pilot study
- are there any alternative explanations for your observations?

Extensions:
- compare fine arts students with other groups

12 Non-parametric tests

Notes for students

A non-parametric test is an hypothesis test in which no assumptions are made about the particular statistical distributions from which the samples are drawn. Typical hypotheses which can be tested using non-parametric methods are:

- a sample is drawn from an unknown distribution with a given median
- two independent samples come from distribution/s having the same median
- two samples come from populations which are identical in form

If the distributions are symmetric the conclusions about medians will also apply to means.

Sign test for median

H_0: population median $= m$
H_1: population median $\neq m$ (or the one-tailed equivalent)

Method
Allocate '+' to each $x_i > m$ and '−' to each $x_i < m$, omitting any $x_i = m$.
r = the number of times the most frequent sign occurs
n = the number of x_i allocated a sign

Decision
Use $B(n, 0.5)$ to find P (r or more). For a two-tailed test, reject H_0 if this probability is less than $\alpha/2$, where α is the significance level.

Note: the test makes no assumptions about the distribution of X. If $n > 25$ use the Normal approximation to $B(n, 0.5)$.

Paired sign test

H_0: median of $d_i = x_i - y_i = 0$
H_1: median of $d_i \neq 0$ (or the one-tailed equivalent)

Method
Examine each pair (x_i, y_i) and find d_i.
Allocate '+' if $d_i > 0$ and '−' if $d_i < 0$, omitting any pair where $x_i = y_i$.
r = the number of times the most frequent sign occurs

n = the number of pairs allocated a sign

Decision
Use $B(n, 0.5)$ to find P (r or more). For a two-tailed test, reject H_0 if this probability is less than $\alpha/2$, where α is the significance level.

Note: The test makes no assumptions about the distribution of d_i nor does it assume that X and Y are drawn from the same population. If $n > 25$ use the Normal approximation to $B(n, 0.5)$.

Wilcoxon signed rank test (for matched pairs data)

H_0: median of $d_i = x_i - y_i = 0$
H_1: median of $d_i \neq 0$ (or the one-tailed equivalent)

Method
For each matched pair (x_i, y_i) find d_i. Rank the d_i without respect to sign. For tied d's assign the average of the tied ranks. Give each rank the sign of the d_i which it represents.
T = the smaller of the sums of like signed ranks
n = the number of d's allocated a sign

Decision
Refer to tables for critical values of T.

Note: The distribution of d_i should be symmetrical. If $n > 25$ use the Normal approximation.

$$z = \frac{T - \dfrac{n(n + 1)}{4}}{\sqrt{\dfrac{n(n + 1)(2n + 1)}{24}}}$$

This test is based on the magnitude of the differences as well as their sign. It is more powerful than the sign test.

The Wilcoxon signed rank test can also be used to test an hypothesis about the median of a (single) symmetric distribution.

Note: For these three tests, observations which cannot be allocated a sign are ignored. It can be argued that such observations support H_o. Hence, if there are many such observations, the validity of the test should be questioned.

Mann Whitney U test (Wilcoxon rank sum test)

$x_1 \ldots x_n$ is a random sample of size n from an unknown continuous distribution with distribution function $F(x)$.

$y_1 \ldots y_m$ is a random sample of size m ($m \geq n$) from an unknown continuous distribution with distribution function $G(y)$.

The data is not paired.
$H_0: F(x) = G(y)$
$H_1: F(x) \neq G(y)$

Method
Rank all of the data (both samples together) giving rank 1 to the lowest score, etc. Find the sum of the ranks, T, for the smaller of the two samples (sample of size n).

Let $U = nm + \dfrac{n(n + 1)}{2} - T$ and $U' = nm - U$.

Decision
If $m < 20$ choose the smaller of U and U' and refer to tables. If $m \geq 20$ use the Normal approximation

$$z = \frac{U - \dfrac{nm}{2}}{\sqrt{\dfrac{nm(n + m + 1)}{12}}}$$

Note: This is one of the more powerful non-parametric tests. The hypothesis is that the distributions are identical in every respect. However, if H_0 is rejected, it indicates a difference in location.

12.1 **Pebbles**

The distinction between sand, pebbles and rocks is a grey area.
As a rule of thumb, a pebble can be defined as being from approximately
0.5 to 10 cm on the long axis.

Requirements:
- pebbly beach

Data collection:
- selecting a starting point at random, walk along the beach at the water's edge and pick up the pebble nearest your toe at each stride. Collect about 10 pebbles
- repeat at about 10 metres from the water's edge. Collect a sample of about 10 pebbles (sample sizes do not need to be the same)
- mark the pebbles clearly to distinguish between the two samples

Analysis:
- arrange the pebbles, by eye, in order of magnitude
- perform the Mann Whitney U test to test whether the pebbles from the water's edge are, on average, smaller than those from further up the beach

Conclusions:
- what are the populations from which your samples were drawn?
- is your method of sampling likely to have introduced any bias?
- discuss the result of your test
- in order to carry out this test, have you made any assumptions about the distribution of pebble sizes?
- is there any other test which you could have used to compare these pebbles?

Extensions:
- calculate some measure (weight, length, roundness) of these pebbles and do an unpaired t-test

12.2 End-of-year examination results

Requirements:
- end-of-year examination results for pupils studying Pure Mathematics and Statistics (or any other pair of subjects). Use about 10 pairs of marks

Data collection:
- record, for each pupil, their mark in Pure Mathematics and their mark in Statistics

Analysis:
- apply the Wilcoxon signed rank test to test whether students score higher on one examination than on the other

Conclusions:
- what is the population from which your sample was drawn?
- is your method of sampling likely to have introduced any bias?
- does the result of your test indicate that there is a difference between student performance in the two examinations?
- give at least two *possible* explanations for differences/similarities found between the students' performances
- did you have to make any assumptions about the distribution of the differences between the two tests?

Extensions:
- apply the sign test and/or the paired *t*-test. Compare the results and assumptions

12.3 **Arm wrestling**

This exercise can be done using most tests requiring strength or skill.

Requirements:
- about 15 pairs of pupils from the same year group

Data collection:
- separate the pupils into an older half and a younger half
- rank pupils according to age in each half and pair them according to rank, for example youngest in group 1 with the youngest in group 2
- each pair takes part in a 'best of 3' arm wrestling competition
- record '+' if the pupil from the older group wins and '−' if the pupil from the younger group wins

Analysis:
- carry out the sign test

Conclusions:
- what is the population from which your sample was drawn?
- is your selection of subjects likely to have introduced any bias?
- does your data support the view that the older contestant is more likely to win?
- why was the sign test used instead of the paired *t*-test or Wilcoxon's signed rank test?
- what is the likely result if the number of pairs is greatly increased?

Extensions:
- increase the sample size by repeating with additional classes
- compare boys with girls of the same age
- try ranking according to some other criteria, such as height or examination results, rather than by age

12.4 Random Normal variables IV

The analysis of data in this exercise is repetitive and best done using a computer program. For this reason, the format of the exercise has been altered.

Requirements:
- computer program to generate random Normal variables or the data sets provided in Table 1 and Table 2 of the Appendix, pp. 132, 134

Section A

Data collection:
- use the computer program to generate 12 pairs of data (x_i, y_i) from the Normal distributions $X \sim N(20,4^2)$, and $Y \sim N(20,4^2)$, or use data from the Appendix
- repeat 100 times to give 100 samples, each of 12 pairs

Analysis:
- for each pair, calculate $d_i = x_i - y_i$
- for each sample test the hypothesis that the median of $d_i = 0$ using
  - *(a)* the sign test
  - *(b)* the Wilcoxon signed rank test
  - *(c)* the paired t-test (remember that, for a Normal distribution, mean = median)
- use 20% significance levels and record the number of times that H_0 is rejected (critical value for two-sided t-test $= \pm 1.364$ critical region for Wilcoxon signed rank test ≤ 22)

Conclusions:
- are the results of the tests consistent with the 20% significance level?

Section B

Data collection and analysis:
- repeat Section A with $X \sim N(20,4^2)$ and $Y \sim N(23,4^2)$

Conclusions:
- compare the three tests, considering the proportion of type II errors made by each of the three tests and
  - *(a)* the assumptions made for each test
  - *(b)* the types of data to which the tests may be applied

Extensions:
- investigate the effect of increasing the sample size
- investigate the effect on type II error of varying the difference between the means of X and Y
- investigate the effect of using non-Normal distributions

12.5 **Births and deaths**

It has been suggested that people who are dying often postpone their death until after a special event, such as a birthday.

Requirements:
- dictionary of biography or some other publication which contains dates of birth and death of individuals

Data collection:
- record the date of birth and the date of death of about 60 people (for the purpose of this exercise the year is of no importance)

Analysis:
- for each person assign a '+' if they died in the 6 months after their birthday and a '−' if they died in the 6 months before their birthday. (You may wish to assume that all months are of equal length)
- use the sign test to test the hypothesis that the median date of death is the same as the date of birth

Conclusions:
- what is the population from which your sample is drawn?
- is your method of sampling likely to have introduced any bias?
- do your results support the view that people may postpone their deaths until after their birthday?

Extensions:
- apply the Wilcoxon signed rank test to test whether the median date of death is the same as the date of birth
- do separate tests for men/women, famous/ordinary people
- use the χ^2 test to test whether dates of death are Uniformly distributed relative to birthdays

12.6 Shopping basket

Requirements:
- a local 'corner shop' selling brand-name products
- a branch of a major supermarket selling the same brand-name products

Data collection:
- price of at least 20 brand-name products from the 'corner shop', x
- price of identical products from a branch of the major supermarket, y. You must decide how to deal with any 'Special offers'

Analysis:
- for each pair, calculate $d_i = x_i - y_i$
- test the hypothesis that the median of $d_i = 0$ using
  - *(a)* the sign test
  - *(b)* the Wilcoxon signed rank test
  - *(c)* the paired t-test (remember that, if the d_i are Normally distributed then mean = median)

Conclusions:
- what are the populations from which your samples were drawn?
- is your method of sampling likely to have introduced any bias?
- compare the three tests, considering the assumptions made for each test
- are supermarket prices lower than those in your corner shop?

Extensions:
- increase the number of products. How does this affect the results of your tests?
- use correlation to examine the relationship between the corner shop prices and those of the supermarket
- compare own-brand and brand-name prices in the supermarket

13 Statistical process control and acceptance sampling

Notes for students

Statistical process control and acceptance sampling are statistical methods used when large numbers of similar items are being produced. **Statistical process control** involves taking samples at regular intervals while production is in progress. The purpose is to identify when adjustments to the production process are necessary in order to avoid producing non-conforming items. **Acceptance sampling** is applied (probably by a customer) to large batches of items after production. The purpose is to check, by examining a sample, whether or not the batch is of acceptable quality.

Both methods can be applied using variables such as lengths, weights, volumes, or attributes (classifying items as conforming or non-conforming)

Note: the terms *conforming* and *non-conforming* have now replaced *non-defective* and *defective*.

Most processes have a target value. For example, in the process of filling cans of cold drink there is a target for the volume of drink in each can. However, every process is subject to some variation. The variability present when a process is running well is called the **short term** or **inherent variability** and is usually measured by the standard deviation. When the process mean is on target and only short term variability is present, the process is said to be 'in control'.

Statistical process control

The most common form of statistical process control involves taking samples of size n at regular intervals and plotting the sample mean on a control chart. The **warning limits** are set at $\mu \pm 1.96\, \sigma/\sqrt{n}$ and the **action limits** at $\mu \pm 3.09\, \sigma/\sqrt{n}$, where μ is the target value and σ is the inherent variability. The warning limits are sometimes called '1 in 40' limits since, assuming the sample mean is Normally distributed, there is a 1 in 40 chance of the sample mean being outside each warning limit if the process mean is on target. Similarly, the action limits are sometimes called '1 in 1000' limits.

A sample mean lying outside the action limits indicates that the process mean has changed and action should be taken to restore it to the target value. A sample mean lying between action and warning limits is a warning that the process mean may have changed and a further sample should be taken immediately to check. If the mean of this further sample lies outside the warning limits action should be taken.

Similarly, the sample standard deviations (or sample ranges) may be plotted on a chart to check whether or not the variability has increased. Limits are used in the same way as on charts for means.

In some cases the target value is unknown or unattainable. For example, if the variable is strength, the target might be 'as great as possible'. In these cases, a large sample is taken when the process is thought to be performing satisfactorily. The mean of this sample is used as the target value and the sample may also be used to estimate the inherent variability. This procedure is known as a **process capability study**.

If attributes are used, the acceptable proportion, p, of non-conforming items is established using a process capability study. The number of non-conforming items in a sample of size n is plotted on charts. The warning limits are $np \pm 1.96\, \sqrt{np(1-p)}$ and the action limits are $np \pm 3.09\, \sqrt{np(1-p)}$. A sample below the lower limits would not be cause for alarm but rather an indication that the process may have improved.

Note: attributes charts can only be used successfully if n and p are reasonably large. If necessary, the value of p can be increased by making the definition of a non-conforming item more severe.

Acceptance sampling

In acceptance sampling, a random sample of size n is taken from a batch of similar items. The batch is rejected if the number of non-conforming items in the sample equals or exceeds r. Otherwise the batch is accepted without further inspection. Providing n is small compared to the size of the batch, the probability of accepting a batch containing a proportion, p, of non-conforming items may be calculated using the Binomial distribution. A graph of probability of acceptance against p is called the **operating characteristic**. The operating characteristic will depend on the values of n and r. These are chosen to give operating characteristics suited to particular circumstances.

Some acceptance sampling plans allow the possibility of taking a second sample before a decision is made. This is known as double sampling. The idea is that very good or very bad batches can be identified by a single sample but a second sample may be necessary to determine the acceptability of an intermediate batch.

Acceptance sampling may also be carried out by taking a random sample and measuring a variable. The batch will be rejected if the sample mean lies outside a predetermined set of values.

In practice, acceptance sampling plans are usually obtained from BS 6001. A table from BS 6001 giving double sampling plans is included with Exercise 13.6 on page 104. To use this table you need to know a code letter (which depends on the batch size) and the Acceptance Quality Level (AQL). The AQL is the percent non-conforming (or, in some cases, the number of non-conformances per hundred items) in a batch which should have a high probability of acceptance. For example, Code Letter K, AQL 1.5% gives the following double sampling plan:

	Sample size	Accept	Reject
First Sample	80	2	5
Second sample	80	6	7

13.1 Simulated data I

You may wish to use this as a class exercise.

Requirements:
- a computer program to generate Binomial data, or
- a Binomial sampling box (a box containing balls of two different colours from which samples may be taken)

Data collection:
- generate 50 samples from $P \sim B(60, 0.15)$
- generate 50 samples from $Q \sim B(60, 0.25)$

Analysis:
- set up a control chart for proportions with a 'target' proportion of 0.15 using a Normal approximation. Show warning and action limits
- plot the proportions on the control chart – P first, followed by Q

Conclusions:
- how many proportions from samples P were outside the warning limits?
- is this consistent with what you would expect from the theory?
- how many proportions from samples Q were outside the warning limits?
- is this consistent with what you would expect from the theory?
- is this chart an effective method of signalling a change in proportions?
- are there any advantages or disadvantages of using an attributes chart rather than a variables chart?
- consider the difference between the 'target' proportion and the actual target

Extensions:
- generate Poisson data and set up charts using a Normal approximation to a Poisson distribution
- set up charts using exact Binomial/Poisson distributions
- set up charts using the proportion of non-conforming items in the first 10 samples to estimate the 'target' proportion
- examine the effect of varying the sample size

13.2 Simulated data II

You may wish to use this as a class exercise.

Requirements:
- a computer program to generate random Normal variables in order to simulate an industrial process, or
- sets of rods with lengths of known distribution which can be used for the same purpose

Data collection:
- generate 10 samples, each of size 4, from $A \sim N(500, 3^2)$
- generate a further 10 samples, each of size 4, from $B \sim N(503, 3^2)$
- generate a further 10 samples, each of size 4, from $C \sim N(500, 6^2)$

Analysis:
- set up a control chart for means of samples of size 4, target value of 500, assuming $\sigma = 3$. Show warning and action limits
- set up a control chart for standard deviations (or ranges if preferred) of samples of size 4 assuming $\sigma = 3$
- calculate the mean for each sample of size 4 (30 means) and plot them on the means chart – A first followed by B and then C
- calculate the standard deviation for each sample and plot them on the standard deviation (range) chart – A first followed by B and then C

Conclusions:
- how many means from samples A were outside the warning limits? Outside the action limits?
  - (a) for your results
  - (b) for the class results if available
- is this consistent with what you would expect from the theory?
- repeat for samples B and samples C
- consider the above questions for the standard deviation (range) charts
- are these charts an effective method of signalling
  - (a) a deviation of the mean from the target?
  - (b) an increase in variability?

Extensions:
- compare the performance of range charts to that of standard deviation charts
- estimate the average run length for the mean and the standard deviation for a variety of deviations from target

13.3 Compact discs

Requirements:
- the data below. This is real production data from a factory producing CD boxes

Data collection:
- data provided is the width, in centimetres, of samples of 4 CD boxes taken at regular intervals from a production line.
  The target value = 118.25

Analysis:
- use the first 10 samples to estimate the short term standard deviation
- use this value to set up a control chart for means of samples of size 4. Show warning and action limits
- set up a control chart for standard deviation (or ranges if preferred) for samples of size 4
- calculate the mean for all of the samples and plot them on the means chart
- calculate the standard deviations (ranges) of all of the samples and plot them on the standard deviation (range) chart

Conclusions:
- did the process appear to be in control for the 10 samples used to estimate the standard deviation?
- did the process appear to remain in control?
- if the process did not appear to remain in control, was effective action taken?

Extensions:
- compare the performance of the standard deviation chart and the range chart
- repeat the exercise using other real production data, if available
- if you have sufficient data, classify data outside a certain limit as non-conforming and set up a chart for attributes

Data for compact disc boxes

Sample	1	2	3	4	5	6	7	8	9	10
Time	7.30	13.45	9.30	17.30	16.00	17.30	8.10	7.00	8.40	16.10
Date	25.4	25.4	26.4	26.4	27.4	28.4	29.4	30.4	1.5	1.5
	118.45	118.45	118.41	118.42	118.46	118.44	118.50	118.44	118.40	118.48
	118.43	118.43	118.39	118.41	118.45	118.43	118.49	118.43	118.46	118.46
	118.45	118.46	118.39	118.42	118.47	118.44	118.50	118.44	118.46	118.48
	118.45	118.40	118.41	118.43	118.52	118.47	118.51	118.43	118.47	118.51

Sample	11	12	13	14	15	16	17	18	19	20
Time	8.30	8.25	14.40	16.50	7.50	8.35	17.40	9.00	14.45	7.30
Date	2.5	3.5	3.5	4.5	5.5	6.5	6.5	7.5	7.5	8.5
	118.15	118.27	118.25	118.28	118.23	118.26	118.27	118.28	118.22	118.26
	118.22	118.25	118.24	118.27	118.25	118.25	118.29	118.22	118.22	118.24
	118.23	118.27	118.24	118.27	118.25	118.26	118.20	118.31	118.21	118.25
	118.23	118.25	118.24	118.27	118.24	118.26	118.25	118.19	118.21	118.24

13.4 **Packets of crisps I**

Requirements:
- table defining tolerable negative errors, see Appendix Table 3a, p. 136
- table giving acceptance sampling plans, see Appendix Tables 3b and 3d, p. 136
- weighing machine
- a batch of at least 100 packets of crisps, or any packaged commodity with specified nominal quantity, such as chocolate bars, soap powder, etc.

Data collection:
- choose an appropriate single sampling plan from the table of acceptance sampling plans
- take a sample of the required size from the batch
- weigh the contents of each packet (weigh an empty packet and subtract this figure from the gross weight of each packet)

Analysis:
- use the nominal weight and Table 3a to find the Tolerable Negative Error, (TNE)
- subtract the TNE from the nominal quantity. Packages containing less than this quantity are called non-standard
- count the number of non-standard packages in your sample

Conclusions:
- what is the population from which the sample is drawn?
- is your method of sampling likely to have introduced any bias?
- did your chosen plan lead you to accept or reject the batch?
- compare the plans for destructive tests with those for non-destructive tests

Extensions:
- repeat using a double sampling plan, see Appendix Table 3c, p. 136

13.5 Packets of crisps II

Requirements:
- table defining tolerable negative error, see Appendix Table 3a, p.136
- table giving plans for acceptance sampling by variable, see Appendix Table 3e or 3f, p. 136
- weighing machine
- a batch of at least 100 packets of crisps, or any packaged commodity with specified nominal quantity, such as chocolate bars, soap powder, etc.

Data collection:
- choose an appropriate plan from the tables of plans for acceptance sampling by variable
- take a sample of the required size from the batch
- weigh the contents of each packet (weigh an empty packet and subtract this figure from the gross weight of each packet)

Analysis:
- calculate σ from your sample
- apply the criteria given in the appropriate table.
  Note: in the table the nominal quantity is denoted Q_n and σ is denoted s

Conclusions:
- what is the population from which the sample is drawn?
- is your method of sampling likely to have introduced any bias?
- did your chosen plan lead you to accept or reject the batch?
- compare the plans for destructive tests with those for non-destructive tests

13.6 Simulated data III

You may wish to use this as a class exercise.

Requirements:
- computer program to generate Binomial data
- BS 6001 table IIIA opposite

Section A

Data collection:
- use BS 6001 table IIIA to select the double sampling plan using code letter G, Acceptance Quality Level 2.5%
- generate an observation from $X \sim B(n, 0.025)$. n is determined by your plan. This observation represents the number of non-conforming items in a sample of size n
- select a second observation if your plan so indicates
- repeat 10 times

Conclusions:
- how many times (out of 10) did your plan accept the batch?
- for pooled class results if available – what proportion of your batches were accepted?
- what proportion of the tests required a second sample to be taken (your own/pooled class data)?
- discuss advantages and disadvantages of a double sampling plan compared to a single sampling plan

Section B

Data collection:
- as for Section A, but with $X \sim B(n, 0.1)$

Conclusions:
- as for Section A
- how effective was your plan at rejecting batches containing 10% non-conforming items?

Section C

Data collection:
- as for Section A, but with $X \sim B(n, 0.01)$

Conclusions:
- as for Section A
- given that batches contain 1% non-conforming items, did the test perform as expected?

Final conclusions:
- discuss the advantages and disadvantages of a double sampling plan compared to a single sampling plan
- comment on the relationship between the proportion of non-conforming items and the proportion of batches rejected by this test

Extensions:
- using plans from BS 6001, compare single, double, multiple and sequential sampling
- compare normal, tightened and reduced inspection

Table IIIA – Double sampling plans for normal inspection (Master table) BS6001: Part 1

Acceptable Quality Levels (normal inspection)

Ac = Acceptance number
Re = Rejection number

(In the table below, each cell gives the First-sample and Second-sample plan as "Ac Re". Blank cells in the original carry the arrow/dot symbols explained in the legend. The numeric acceptance/rejection entries are reproduced along the staircase diagonal of the master table.)

Code	Sample	Sample size	Cum. sample size	0.010	0.015	0.025	0.040	0.065	0.10	0.15	0.25	0.40	0.65	1.0	1.5	2.5	4.0	6.5	10	15	25	40	65	100	150	250	400	650	1000
A																											
B	First	2	2																	0 2	0 3	1 4	2 5	3 7	5 9	7 11	11 16	17 22	25 31
B	Second	2	4																	1 2	3 4	4 5	6 7	8 9	12 13	18 19	26 27	37 38	56 57
C	First	3	3																0 2	0 3	1 4	2 5	3 7	5 9	7 11	11 16	17 22	25 31	
C	Second	3	6																1 2	3 4	4 5	6 7	8 9	12 13	18 19	26 27	37 38	56 57	
D	First	5	5															0 2	0 3	1 4	2 5	3 7	5 9	7 11	11 16	17 22	25 31		
D	Second	5	10															1 2	3 4	4 5	6 7	8 9	12 13	18 19	26 27	37 38	56 57		
E	First	8	8														0 2	0 3	1 4	2 5	3 7	5 9	7 11	11 16	17 22	25 31			
E	Second	8	16														1 2	3 4	4 5	6 7	8 9	12 13	18 19	26 27	37 38	56 57			
F	First	13	13													0 2	0 3	1 4	2 5	3 7	5 9	7 11	11 16	17 22	25 31				
F	Second	13	26													1 2	3 4	4 5	6 7	8 9	12 13	18 19	26 27	37 38	56 57				
G	First	20	20												0 2	0 3	1 4	2 5	3 7	5 9	7 11	11 16	17 22	25 31					
G	Second	20	40												1 2	3 4	4 5	6 7	8 9	12 13	18 19	26 27	37 38	56 57					
H	First	32	32											0 2	0 3	1 4	2 5	3 7	5 9	7 11	11 16	17 22	25 31						
H	Second	32	64											1 2	3 4	4 5	6 7	8 9	12 13	18 19	26 27	37 38	56 57						
J	First	50	50										0 2	0 3	1 4	2 5	3 7	5 9	7 11	11 16	17 22	25 31							
J	Second	50	100										1 2	3 4	4 5	6 7	8 9	12 13	18 19	26 27	37 38	56 57							
K	First	80	80									0 2	0 3	1 4	2 5	3 7	5 9	7 11	11 16	17 22	25 31								
K	Second	80	160									1 2	3 4	4 5	6 7	8 9	12 13	18 19	26 27	37 38	56 57								
L	First	125	125								0 2	0 3	1 4	2 5	3 7	5 9	7 11	11 16	17 22	25 31									
L	Second	125	250								1 2	3 4	4 5	6 7	8 9	12 13	18 19	26 27	37 38	56 57									
M	First	200	200							0 2	0 3	1 4	2 5	3 7	5 9	7 11	11 16	17 22	25 31										
M	Second	200	400							1 2	3 4	4 5	6 7	8 9	12 13	18 19	26 27	37 38	56 57										
N	First	315	315						0 2	0 3	1 4	2 5	3 7	5 9	7 11	11 16	17 22	25 31											
N	Second	315	630						1 2	3 4	4 5	6 7	8 9	12 13	18 19	26 27	37 38	56 57											
P	First	500	500					0 2	0 3	1 4	2 5	3 7	5 9	7 11	11 16	17 22	25 31												
P	Second	500	1000					1 2	3 4	4 5	6 7	8 9	12 13	18 19	26 27	37 38	56 57												
Q	First	800	800				0 2	0 3	1 4	2 5	3 7	5 9	7 11	11 16	17 22	25 31													
Q	Second	800	1600				1 2	3 4	4 5	6 7	8 9	12 13	18 19	26 27	37 38	56 57													
R	First	1250	1250			0 2	0 3	1 4	2 5	3 7	5 9	7 11	11 16	17 22	25 31														
R	Second	1250	2500			1 2	3 4	4 5	6 7	8 9	12 13	18 19	26 27	37 38	56 57														

⇩ = Use first sampling plan below arrow. If sample size equals or exceeds lot or batch size, do 100 percent inspection.

⇧ = Use first sampling plan above arrow.

• = Use corresponding single sampling plan (or alternatively, use double sampling plan below, where available).

Ac = Acceptance number
Re = Rejection number

13.7 Re-formed scampi

Requirements:
- data for pack weights of frozen re-formed scampi of nominal weight 454 g, opposite. Data is provided for 4 batches each of size 200

Data collection:
- take a random sample of size 25 from batch 1 and estimate the standard deviation
- use the estimated standard deviation to define a non-conforming packet in such a way that a batch of mean 454 g will contain about 20% non-conforming packets
- design a single sampling plan with sample size 25 which will have a probability of approximately 0.95 of accepting a batch containing 20% non-conforming items
- take a random sample from each of batches 2, 3 and 4 and apply the plan

Conclusions:
- did you accept or reject the batches?
- discuss the advantage of having a large proportion of non-conforming items in an acceptable batch

Extensions:
- take repeated samples from batches 2, 3 and 4 and apply your plan. Find the mean and standard deviation of each batch and relate them to the proportion of times that the plan is accepted

Pack weights of frozen re-formed scampi

Batch 1

453.97	458.3	453.42	452.01	450.66
453.19	452.27	452.42	451.5	454.56
457.56	452.01	452.32	451.9	455.09
453.45	452.96	454.81	450.75	452.81
454.32	457	456.83	454.33	453.3
448.82	456.85	454.2	454.84	455.01
454.05	454.91	453.76	455.73	455.61
452.16	456.84	451.2	451.03	454.92
456.17	452.08	454.44	451.89	456.44
454.48	455.12	455.77	452.48	454.44
450.96	453.63	454.78	458.97	455.73
450.27	454.27	456.94	455.04	450.45
454.84	457.13	452.48	454.27	457.79
453.46	455.37	454.65	455.38	457.65
455.62	453.31	452.93	455.46	453.11
452.03	453.7	459.07	453.03	455.09
453.86	452.92	455.61	456.29	453.55
455.61	454.11	452.91	455.79	454.75
453.59	452.38	455.55	455.15	450.85
453.17	451.63	451.63	457.73	456.2
458.11	455.94	452.59	453.33	453.89
456.14	452.02	457.59	454.33	452.97
456.3	454.04	458.84	456.61	454.28
452.97	455.83	455.38	454.76	452.17
455.59	451.3	451.3	454.97	454.75
452.96	453.35	454.28	451.97	453.82
457.7	454.71	453.91	452.3	451.53
453.09	453.75	448.86	450.12	452.06
452.25	454.03	458.01	458.21	454.9
455.93	454.47	455.47	453.13	453.76
455.16	453.78	456.28	452.02	455.52
455.02	456.79	453.59	456.42	450.57
454.28	450.89	455.25	455.8	452.93
451.64	451.07	456.87	453.07	455.4
455.34	452.97	452.82	457.66	457.84
458.12	452.6	458.21	450.64	453.67
451.6	451.92	453.38	453.07	450.25
452.96	452.67	458	453	455.4
452.52	457.37	452.46	452.28	454.98
454.63	455.67	452.38	456.32	451.52

Batch 2

453.09	452.24	449.78	450.36	449.64
452.28	450.89	452.81	450.63	451.51
446.9	448.91	447.11	452.28	451.14
452.96	450.75	448.36	449.96	452.49
451.26	452.45	449.87	451.93	451.51
451.35	449.98	450.72	451.69	450.36
452.49	451.54	448.43	450.21	448.99
450.63	447.98	448.85	450.4	453.08
449.16	451.61	452.7	451.42	450.21
449.26	449.39	450.53	452.57	451.33
449.39	451.92	449.19	449.54	450.54
449.83	449.93	453.51	453.24	447.88
453.46	452.16	452.82	450.26	449.33
451.78	452.24	448.05	450.45	450.82
451.34	449.3	450.65	447.45	447.36
455.38	452.92	451.14	449.75	449.49
450.98	453.88	450.07	449.82	454.16
449.55	447.09	451.24	451.01	452.5
454.92	453.34	447.78	447.81	451.96
449.74	452.55	451.81	451.23	454.37
451.03	450.3	448.34	450.56	452.17
450.15	450.77	451.79	449.96	451.57
449.38	450.97	452.52	450.83	450.63
450.36	452.2	450.61	453.23	449.24
452.82	449.41	450.65	455.06	451.12
451.5	451.57	450.61	447.95	452.34
449.84	452.12	449.94	448.84	449.36
452.59	450.12	448.66	451.66	451.92
450.5	450.47	449.46	447.42	453.22
447.92	453.89	452.06	455.07	452.68
452.25	447.86	451.97	452.64	450.91
451.27	450.25	450.28	450.07	451.12
451.77	449.32	452.49	451.23	452.02
449.75	450.59	449.44	449.48	450.6
449.78	450.25	453.29	453.09	453.26
452.96	452.71	453.15	451.53	449.33
451.32	451.75	447.06	447.85	446.59
451.57	451.59	452.94	447.36	450.84
450.32	451.36	449.24	452.17	452.07
451.24	448.84	456.47	452.21	451.19

Batch 3

455.65	457.17	456.77	463.09	456.04
460.75	456.65	457.02	459.1	456.1
460.36	456.73	455.14	456.3	459.26
457.26	458.02	457.7	455.78	458.86
458.09	455.74	453.93	462.22	458.79
459.58	454.47	459.35	457.59	457.5
456.86	458.08	455.67	455.02	460.01
458.99	455.9	456.33	456.92	461.57
456.29	456.38	454.21	457.48	457.95
457.85	456.84	456.86	456.75	456.5
459.89	456.12	457.46	461.07	459.7
457.29	459.3	459.26	457.45	459.7
455.1	457.38	452.24	457.03	455.28
460.89	456.94	456.1	458.18	456.99
456.7	460.94	458.76	456.24	458.27
457.07	460.07	459.2	459.2	457.2
454.1	457.35	458.08	461.38	459.06
458.49	457.54	458.76	458.84	461.08
457.52	459.62	457.81	459.78	462
461.86	459	457.66	454.19	457.66
459.06	456.57	461.44	456.85	458.63
456.15	456.92	458.25	454.51	459.53
457.49	456.1	456.57	460.35	455.22
455.39	456.31	457.51	457.52	459.21
453.24	460.86	454.65	459.63	457.36
457.69	458.82	455.85	456.63	456.04
455.59	457.11	457.54	457.98	458.81
456.6	460.75	460.13	463.68	457.87
455.93	458.3	458.82	458.82	458.99
456.49	455.22	459.71	461.25	460.98
462.12	457.54	456.99	457.76	460.28
459.17	456.1	453.69	461.24	461.02
460.35	458.43	457.58	457.58	455.01
458.83	456.18	456.14	456.54	457.31
460.53	460.1	458.08	459.18	460.51
461.95	459.89	462.39	458.79	458.05
457.49	459.42	462.16	462.16	456.45
457.21	456.25	460.22	457.5	454.56
458.76	461.53	461.07	458.64	460.88
461.63	456.06	455.96	456.24	458.83

Batch 4

449.55	459.32	458.95	444.17	457.86
456.09	454.28	451.83	447.6	452.61
447.35	458.69	451.97	451.39	453.26
449.34	458.81	462.8	449.44	453.8
451.66	457.7	453.64	454.62	460.87
447.75	448.48	452.71	452.56	457.92
457.07	451.43	452.62	456.45	456.56
458.93	450.26	452.11	455.24	455.32
454.18	457.9	449.9	454.92	454.24
450.29	458.81	449.96	456.81	449.62
448.68	450.43	454.36	454.87	453.47
451.52	452.36	451.5	454.32	453.08
451.96	456.24	451.97	460.75	462.95
454.36	458.19	458.18	453.78	438.12
447.36	461.71	461.37	455.29	453.95
454.62	451.58	446.11	451.64	455.58
458.98	453.1	453.5	443.91	465.89
452.7	461.55	452.7	456.88	448.39
460.05	458.13	446.74	451.3	449.88
445.56	445.78	458.07	461.17	458.41
449.12	458.72	447.41	452.98	458.37
453.34	454.64	452.56	456.31	461.36
455.31	457.04	452.15	457.1	452.48
459.47	455.88	455.48	458.12	458.98
464.2	450.52	454.16	451.55	449.01
450.57	454.07	447.02	451.05	458.92
457.25	455.76	452.27	454.17	455.39
448.22	456.42	452.44	449.12	447.05
448.51	446.96	457.28	460.73	463.37
453.09	452.01	457.62	441.88	444.96
445.05	449.11	459.19	454.08	449.75
457.52	455.17	462.64	459.01	456.09
460.4	445.77	451.56	451.8	456.87
459.98	448.49	448.02	448.99	465.17
458.23	447.67	455.78	463.42	451.92
455.25	460.99	453.54	451.93	456.34
457.47	457.96	461.01	457.41	457.55
450.74	453.01	449.55	451.35	454.85
457.97	454.47	452.38	448.65	459.28
459.16	450.08	457.8	452.94	451.88

14 Student Reports

14.1 Journey times

Diagrams 1:

	lcb < t < ucb	X (f)	Y (f)	Z (f)
15 – 17	14.5 < t < 17.5	–	1	1
18 – 20	17.5 < t < 20.5	–	5	5
21 – 23	20.5 < t < 23.5	3	11	14
24 – 26	23.5 < t < 26.5	12	7	19
27 – 29	26.5 < t < 29.5	5	–	5
30 – 32	29.5 < t < 32.5	4	2	6
33 – 35	32.5 < t < 35.5	2	2	4
36 – 38	35.5 < t < 38.5	1	–	1
39 – 41	38.5 < t < 41.5	1	–	1
42 – 44	41.5 < t < 44.5	1	–	1

	lcb < t < ucb	X (cf)	Y (cf)	Z (cf)
15 – 17	14.5 < t < 17.5	–	1	1
18 – 20	17.5 < t < 20.5	–	6	6
21 – 23	20.5 < t < 23.5	3	17	20
24 – 26	23.5 < t < 26.5	15	24	39
27 – 29	26.5 < t < 29.5	20	24	44
30 – 32	29.5 < t < 32.5	24	26	50
33 – 35	32.5 < t < 35.5	26	28	54
36 – 38	35.5 < t < 38.5	27	28	55
39 – 41	38.5 < t < 41.5	28	28	56
42 – 44	41.5 < t < 44.5	29	28	57

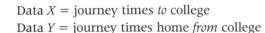

Data X = journey times *to* college
Data Y = journey times home *from* college

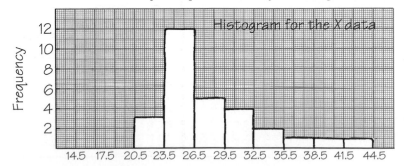

Teacher's comments

Data well presented in tables. A brief introduction would have helped the report.

Unequal class intervals should be considered. In this case, the choice of intervals is satisfactory.

The table has not been presented in the order suggested in the exercise. This presentation is clear and acceptable.

*Labelling clumsy
'X represents journey times to college'
'Y represents journey times home from college'
would be better.*

*Horizontal axes have not been labelled.
Vertical axes represent frequency density, not frequency.*

However, the histograms are aligned and drawn to the same scale, making comparison easy.

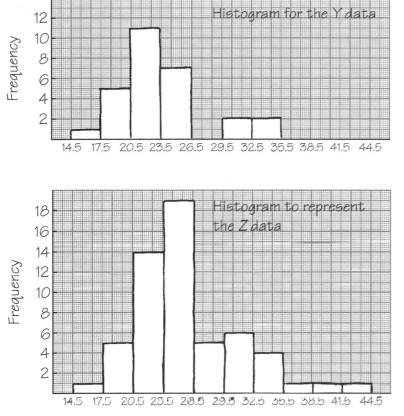

Comments:

The histogram for Z is unimodal. There is one peak between 23.5 min and 26.5 min. The histogram is slightly skewed. The skew is a positive skew. I believe that there are outliers. They seem to occur between 35.5 min and 44.5 min.

The histograms for X and Y are fairly different in their appearance. The *mode* time for the X data is between 21 and 24 minutes, so it is approximately 22.5 minutes. Similarly the *mode* time for the Y data is approximately the same. This is *not* how they differ.

The histogram for the X data has a very positive skewed distribution and is unimodal. There are outliers.

However, the histogram for the Y data is bimodal. It doesn't seem to be very skewed because of it being bimodal, however, it could be said that it has a positive skew.

The outliers on the histogram of the X data explain the outliers on the histogram of Z. They also explain the extremely positive skew. Both modes being approximately the same explains the high peak on histogram Z.

Have confidence – there are outliers in the upper tail.

There is an error here. The 'modal class' is 23.5 to 26.5, so the mode is approximately 24.5 min. In fact, there is a small difference.

The conclusion is correct.

Correct but probably the student is reading too much into such a small amount of data. Variability has not been considered.

Good!

Diagrams 2:

A back to back stem-and-leaf diagram

	Data *X*			Data *Y*
15 – 19		1	5 8	
20 – 24	4 4 4 4 4 4 4 3 2 1	2	0 0 0 0 1 1 1 1 1 2 2 2 2 3 4 4	
25 – 29	8 8 7 7 7 6 6 6 5 5	2	5 5 5 5 5	
30 – 34	3 3 2 0 0 0	3	0 0 3	
35 – 39	8	3	5	
40 – 45	4 0	4		

By reducing the number of class intervals the shapes of the diagrams have been slightly altered. This would be less marked if there were more data. In this case 6 intervals gives a smoother curve than 10 intervals.

Comments:

The fact that it seemed to generally take less time to get home from college is better illustrated on the stem-and-leaf diagram than on the histograms. I think that the difference is that frequency is best shown on the histograms.

The meaning of the final sentence is not clear.

Diagrams 3:

$$\text{median} = \frac{n+1}{2}\text{th position} = \text{15th position}$$

Lower quartile Upper quartile
$Q_1 = 7.5$th position $Q_3 = 22.5$th position

This is an acceptable method. Some texts locate quartiles slightly differently.

From the graph:
$Q_1 = 25.3$
median $= 26.5$
$Q_3 = 30.7$

Cumulative frequency curves are useful for this purpose. They are of little use for comparison and give minimal information on the shape of the distribution.

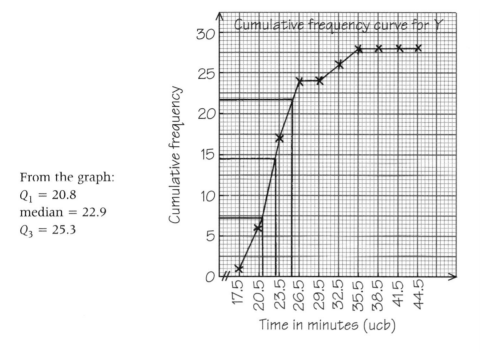

From the graph:
$Q_1 = 20.8$
median $= 22.9$
$Q_3 = 25.3$

NB   Slight inaccuracies must be allowed for when reading from the graph.

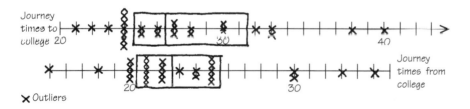

I have used the calculated values from Q_2, Q_1 and Q_3.

Comments:

The box and whisker plot for the X data shows a very positive skew. There are a few outliers. The average journey time to college is shown to be longer that the average journey time home from college.

The box and whisker plot for the Y data *doesn't* show a definite skew. There are also a few outliers. The outliers on both plots give a very misleading picture of the times taken.

The student seems to have plotted the raw data as a sort of dot plot and then superimposed the box and whisker diagram. This should have produced an effective diagram.
Unfortunately the extent of the whiskers is unclear. She has attempted to indicate outliers using a larger X.

Numerical measures:

Median Z   29th position – 23.5 to 26.5

$$\frac{29 - 20}{39 - 20} = \frac{m - 23.5}{26.5 - 23.5} \qquad \frac{9}{19} = \frac{m - 23.5}{3} \qquad m = 24.9$$

$Q_1 Z$ 14.5th position – 20.5 – 23.5

$$\frac{14.5 - 6}{20 - 6} = \frac{Q_1 - 20.5}{23.5 - 20.5} \qquad Q_1 = 22.3$$

$Q_3 Z$ 43.5th position – 26.5 – 29.5

$$\frac{43.5 - 39}{44 - 39} = \frac{Q_3 - 26.5}{3} \qquad Q_3 = 29.2$$

	mean	sd	median	IQ range	mode	range
X	27.9	5.36	26.5	5.4	24	23
Y	23.3	4.29	22.9	4.5	21	20
Z	25.6	5.39	24.9	6.9	24	29

Conclusions:

I think that the box and whisker plots best compare the distributions of *X* and *Y*. I think that the mean and SD best summarise the differences between the distributions of *X* and *Y*. I think that it is important that the outliers are included because journey times are, in reality, very varied.

On reviewing my conclusions with regard to the disruptive features (the main one being a diversion following by travelling by car as opposed to coach one day), I think perhaps that the median and IQ range might give a fairer picture of the *average time taken*. (However it must still be remembered that they do not put as much importance on the outliers as the mean and SD.) The journey times would not be so skewed if the disruptive features had not occurred.

The student has estimated the median and quartiles for Z by linear interpolation. The cumulative frequency curve method, as used with X and Y is equally acceptable.

It appears that the student used the raw data for estimates of mode and range.
This is acceptable for the range but, for the mode of a small data set, it is preferable to use a method based on the modal class.

The student has not noted that all three measures of location indicate that the average value of X is greater than the average value of Y. The same is true for variability.

The student has correctly noted the effect of outliers on numerical measures but has avoided drawing a final conclusion. No attempt has been made to define the population or to discuss possible bias.

Overall a thorough, carefully produced piece of work.

Day	Date	am/pm	Time dep.	Time arr.	Weather	Unusual circumstances	Total time
Mon	12.9	am	8.05	8.35			30
		pm	4.15	4.40			25
Tue	13.9	am	8.05	8.38			33
		pm	3.30	4.05			35
Wed	14.9	am	8.04	8.48		road blocked diversion	44
		pm	4.20	4.44			24
Thurs	15.9	am	8.05	8.33			28
		pm	4.20	4.45			25
Fri	16.9	am	8.30	9.02		coach was late	32
		pm	4.20	4.53			33
Mon	19.9	am	8.05	8.38			33
		pm	5.30	6.00		road blocked	30
Tue	20.9	am	8.05	8.35			30
		pm	3.32	3.52			20
Wed	21.9	am	8.05	8.43			38
		pm	4.20	4.50			30
Thurs	22.9	am	8.06	8.46			40
		pm	4.20	4.42			22
Fri	23.9	am	8.04	8.34			30
		pm	4.20	4.45			25
Mon	26.9	am	8.06	8.33		road blocked	27
		pm	4.21	4.43			22
Tue	27.9	am	8.06	8.34			28
		pm	3.30	3.51			21
Wed	28.9	am	8.07	8.31			24
		pm	4.22	4.42			20
Thurs	29.9	am	8.06	8.30			24
		pm	4.20	4.38			18
Fri	30.9	am	8.06	8.28			22
		pm	4.20	4.40			20

Day	Date	am/pm	Time dep.	Time arr.	Weather	Unusual circumstances	Total time
Mon	3.10	am	8.06	8.30	rain	diversion	24
		pm	4.17	4.38			21
Tue	4.10	am	8.06	8.32			26
		pm	3.30	3.51			21
Wed	5.10	am	8.07	8.34			27
Thurs	6.10	pm	4.19	4.40			21
Fri	7.10	am	8.06	8.29			23
		pm	6.10	6.32		late coach traffic	22
Mon	10.10	am	8.06	8.31			25
		pm	8.25	8.40		late evening car	15
Tue	11.10	am	8.05	3.30			25
		pm	3.29	3.54			25
Wed	12.10	am	8.06	8.30			24
		pm	3.30	5.55			25
Thurs	13.10	am	8.05	8.26			21
		pm	4.18	4.39			21
Fri	14.10	am	8.06	8.30			24
		pm	5.35	5.57			22
Mon	17.10	am	8.07	8.33			26
		pm	4.18	4.38			20
Tue	18.10	am	8.06	8.30			24
		pm	3.29	3.50			21
Wed	19.10	am	8.05	8.31			26
		pm	5.31	5.55			24
Thurs	20.10	am	8.06	8.33			27
		pm	4.18	4.41			23
Fri	21.10	am	8.04	8.28			24

Raw data is available but does not clutter up the main body of the report. Good.

14.2 Satellite TV

Aim:

To collect data off 150 students from this school in the following question – "Do you have satellite TV at home?" Having done this, represent the data in a table and then a graph. Then analyse the derived data and come to any conclusions.

Data collection:

Having produced 6 surveys for the data collection stage, I distributed them to the following classes 1U, 2S, 3P, 3B, 4L and 5H.

Unfortunately I only received back 3 surveys from 1U, 4L and 5H. I therefore had to share results to try to make up the 150 subjects. In future I will try and improve on the data collection stage. I eventually ended up with 1U, 4L, 5H, 5L and 3U, 25 students short of the required number. When choosing the classes it was important not to ask any brothers the same question. I therefore originally aimed the survey at as many different houses as possible. I managed to do this but ended up with 4L, 5L and 3U, 1U.

Analysis: Order of forms – 1U, 3U, 4L, 5H, 5L

Results table to show proportion of students with satellite TV

No. of subjects asked (cumulative), n	5	10	15	20	25	30	35	40	45	50
No. with satellite TV out of n subjects, x	2	4	7	10	13	14	17	19	22	23
Proportion of total with satellite TV, $\frac{x}{n}$	0.40	0.40	0.47	0.50	0.52	0.47	0.49	0.48	0.47	0.44

No. of subjects asked (cumulative), n	55	60	65	70	75	80	85	90	95	100
No. with satellite TV out of n subjects, x	23	24	25	26	26	28	31	32	34	35
Proportion of total with satellite TV, $\frac{x}{n}$	0.42	0.40	0.38	0.37	0.35	0.35	0.36	0.36	0.36	0.35

Teacher's comments

To state the 'aim' of the exercise, is a good way to begin a report.

Quite a lot of thought has been given to the data collection although the description is difficult to follow, particularly if you are not familiar with the organisation of the school. The student has used a 'data collection sheet' for each class, which is incorrectly called a 'survey'.

The data is well presented, using the table given in the instructions.

No. of subjects asked (cumulative), n	105	110	115	120	125
No. with satellite TV out of n subjects, x	37	39	41	43	44
Proportion of total with satellite TV, $\frac{x}{n}$	0.35	0.35	0.36	0.36	0.35

The proportion of students who have satellite TV is $\frac{44}{125}$ or 35%

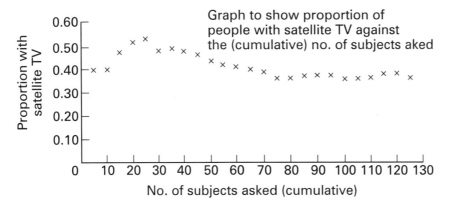

A good, well labelled graph.

Conclusions:

The points on the graph did not lie in a straight line. The proportion rose from 40% to 52% (which was the highest proportion) but then slowly decreased to around 36% where it steadied off and finally ended at 35%. The way in which the graph was plotted depended very much upon the order of the forms. For example, if I had done the graph the opposite way round e.g. 5L, 5H, 4L, 3U, 1U, the graph would have looked different (not necessarily a straight line) but would still have ended up with a final proportion of 35%. Basically, as 'n' increased, the proportion increased to 52% ($n = 25$) then decreased to 35% ($n = 75$) where it changed to 36.035 and ended up at 35%.

By using the line, my estimation for the proportion of the student population which have satellite TV is as follows: the more subjects asked, the more accurate the estimation. Therefore the proportion would be estimated at 35% which is the value for 125 pupils.

Ques. Is it reasonable to suppose that your work is representative of the student population of (a) school (b) your community (c) the UK?

Ans. (a) school – I would say that it is representative of the school. The reason being that most of the students who attend the school are of the same class and ideals. A range of people were asked, e.g. varying ages.

Basically, this is a good discussion although it is not necessary to describe the small fluctuations as they are illustrated on the graph.

Good comment on the order of data entry.

The 'line' is referred to in the instructions for this exercise. It would have been sensible to have drawn the line on the graph.

These are thorough conclusions. However, addressing the points in turn, some in Question and Answer form, makes a disjointed report.

Around 10% of the student population were asked. It should be worthy to note that freak values may have occurred.

(b) community – In my opinion it is not, to a certain extent, representative of the community. Only a sample from our school was surveyed. If all schools in Barnet were surveyed, the case may be different. Another point is that our school is a boy's school.

(c) UK – I would say that it is definitely not representative of the UK. We only sampled one age group, one sex and in one specific school. In order for it to be representative of the UK, all of the students in the UK should be surveyed in every region and also in other 'types' of schools e.g. primary, grammar, comprehensive.

It is rather evident from the results that satellite TV is rather popular amongst students at this school. This is not only true of the 125 students at this school but it is a fair representation of the whole school.

It is not necessary to interview all students (a census) but data from all of these groups would be included in a representative sample.

Overall, a good piece of work.

14.3 Weighted containers

Data collection:

5 pairs of weighted containers, each pair identical in shape and weight and labelled A and B. Each pair had a different weight to any other pair.

30 subjects were chosen, all of them students of the same age and sex. The first subject was told to lift container A and replace it. Then lift container B and replace it. The subject was asked to state which container was heavier and the results were recorded (see Appendix). This was repeated for the other four pairs of containers.

This was repeated for the other subjects.

Analysis:

x	0	1	2	3	4	5
Observed f	6	9	7	5	3	0

X = the number of times that the first (A) container is chosen out of 5 trials.

For the frequency distribution:

$$\text{mean, } \bar{x} = \frac{\sum fx}{\sum f}$$

$$= \frac{(0\times6) + (1\times9) + (2\times7) + (3\times5) + (4\times3) + (5\times0)}{30}$$

$$= \frac{50}{30}$$

$$= 1\tfrac{2}{3}$$

$X \sim B(n, p)$ with $n = 5$

so the mean $E(X) = 1\tfrac{2}{3} = np$

$$np = 1\tfrac{2}{3}$$
$$5p = 1\tfrac{2}{3}$$
$$p = \tfrac{1}{3} = 0.333$$

Calculate the distribution of expected frequencies based on $X \sim \text{Bin}(5, p)$ of 0, 1, 2, 3, 4, 5 using the associated theoretical binomial distribution

Using $P(X = x) = {}^nC_x\, p^x\, (q)^{n-x}$

$P(X = 0) = {}^5C_0\, 0.33^0\, 0.67^{5-0} = 0.135$
$P(X = 1) = {}^5C_1\, 0.33^1\, 0.67^{5-1} = 0.333$
$P(X = 2) = {}^5C_2\, 0.33^2\, 0.67^{5-2} = 0.328$
$P(X = 3) = {}^5C_3\, 0.33^3\, 0.67^{5-3} = 0.161\,32$
$P(X = 4) = {}^5C_4\, 0.33^4\, 0.67^{5-4} = 0.0397$
$P(X = 5) = {}^5C_5\, 0.33^5\, 0.67^{5-5} = 0.003\,91$

Teacher's comments

Some description of the containers/weights used would have added interest.

Although we are told that these are students of the same sex and age, the population is not defined. Whether or not these subjects are likely to be representative of the population is not discussed. The student could have stated 'although the sample was not randomly selected, there was no obvious bias in my choice of subjects'.

The calculations are correct and well presented.

*For more advanced exercises, only the **results** of routine calculations should be given (detailed calculations, if included, should be put in an appendix.)*

The conditions for the Binomial distribution could have been discussed here. (There is some discussion in the conclusions.)

More significant figures should have been used for p in the calculations. For example, $P(X = 0) = 0.132$ to 3dp.

However, it is sensible to round the result to 3 dp.

To obtain theoretical distribution multiply each of the probabilities by the total frequency, 30

x	0	1	2	3	4	5
Theoretical f	4.05	9.96	9.84	4.84	1.19	0.18
	4	10	10	5	1	0

These results compare reasonably well with the original frequency distribution.

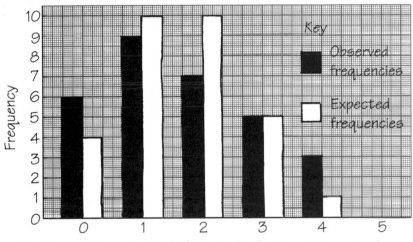

Number of times (out of 5) that the first container is chosen

Conclusions:

From the data obtained, it can be seen that when the two objects are lifted, one after the other, the second is usually judged to be heavier than the first. The calculated value of p, being 0.33 backs up this suggestion about the perception of weight.

However, although this pattern can be seen in the results, it is not an especially strong pattern as in one third of the trials, the subject thought that the first object was heavier than the second.

The data does fit a Binomial model because there are only two outcomes to the trial – people either choose the first or the second object to be heavier (we did not give them the choice to say that they were the same weight). The number of trials is fixed and the fact that the trials are independent also show that this data fits a Binomial model.

The student has rounded the expected (theoretical) frequencies to whole numbers. This is not good practice. Values should be given to at least 1, but preferably 2 decimal places.

It would have been useful to have included the observed frequencies in this table, for comparison.

This is a good diagram, facilitating visual comparisons. Note that a histogram would have been incorrect as the variable is discrete.

The student has not commented on her diagram.

The first two paragraphs of the conclusions are concise and relevant.

The student has correctly noted that there are two outcomes and a fixed number of trials. The fact that the data fits the Binomial distribution reasonably well shows that the assumptions of independence and constant p are plausible. The student has failed to make this connection, merely stating that the trials are independent.

Appendix

Data collected: Which container is thought to be heavier A or B?

Number	1	2	3	4	5	number of A
1	B	B	A	B	B	1
2	B	A	B	A	B	2
3	A	B	B	B	A	2
4	B	A	B	B	B	1
5	A	B	B	A	A	3
6	B	B	B	B	B	0
7	B	A	B	A	B	2
8	B	A	B	A	A	3
9	B	B	B	B	B	0
10	B	A	B	B	B	1
11	A	A	B	B	A	3
12	B	A	A	A	A	4
13	A	B	B	B	A	2
14	B	A	B	B	B	1
15	B	B	A	B	B	1
16	B	B	B	B	B	0
17	B	B	A	B	B	1
18	A	B	B	B	B	1
19	A	A	A	B	A	4
20	B	B	B	A	B	1
21	A	B	B	B	B	1
22	B	B	B	B	B	0
23	B	A	B	A	A	3
24	A	A	B	B	B	2
25	B	B	B	B	B	0
26	B	A	B	A	B	2
27	B	B	B	A	A	2
28	A	B	B	A	A	3
29	B	A	A	A	A	4
30	B	B	B	B	B	0

Good use of an appendix. The raw data is available here but does not clutter up the main body of the report.

14.4 **Estimating length**

Analysis:

	Mean	Standard deviation
7 cm estimate, x	5.8	1.41
17 cm estimate, y	14.4	1.72
difference, z	8.6	2.10

7 cm estimate

Midpoint	3.25	3.75	4.25	4.75	5.25	5.75	6.25
Frequency	1	1	5	4	13	5	6
z value	−1.81	−1.45	−1.10	−.74	−.39	−.04	0.32
$P(X<z)$	.0351	.0735	.1357	.2296	.3483	.484	.6255
$P(X<z)\times 50$	1.8	3.7	6.8	11.5	17.4	24.2	31.3
P not cum	1.8	1.9	3.1	4.7	5.9	6.8	7.1

Midpoint	6.75	7.25	7.75	8.25	8.75	9.25	9.75
Frequency	4	1	1	1	2	1	1
z value	0.67	1.02	1.38	1.74	2.09	2.45	2.8
$P(X<z)$	.7486	.8461	.9162	.9591	.9817	.9929	.9974
$P(X<z)\times 50$	37.4	42.3	45.8	48.0	49.1	49.6	49.9
P not cum	6.1	4.9	3.5	2.19	1.1	0.5	0.3

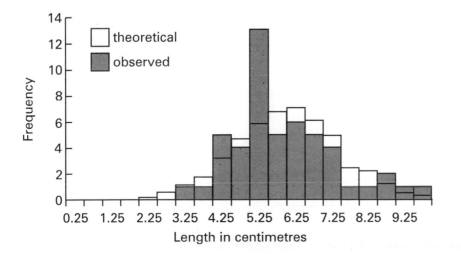

Teacher's comments

Students should begin a presentation with an introduction stating an aim and/or some description of data collection.

The student has interchanged X and Y (see the exercise Estimating Length. This is not important.)

This table appears to be quite comprehensive but there are in fact many errors:
(i) class intervals are not given anywhere
(ii) z values should be calculated from class boundaries, not midpoints
(iii) probabilities should be calculated for −∞ to +∞. This is particularly noticeable for the Y data where the upper tail has been omitted
(iv) the last two rows of this table are expected frequencies, not probabilities (as labelled).

Throughout this report the labelling is inadequate.

There are errors in plotting the frequencies and the numbering of the horizontal axis is unsatisfactory.

Midpoint	10.75	11.25	11.75	12.25	12.75	13.25	13.75
Frequency	1	3	0	2	5	2	4
P($X < x$)	0.02	0.03	0.06	0.12	0.17	0.25	0.35
Cum prob	0.85	1.68	3.08	5.28	8.43	12.59	17.64
Prob	0.81	0.83	1.4	2.2	3.15	4.16	5.05

Midpoint	14.25	14.75	15.25	15.75	16.25	16.75	17.25	17.75
Frequency	6	6	6	7	2	2	2	2
P($X < x$)	0.47	0.58	0.69	0.78	0.86	0.91	0.95	0.97
Cum prob	23.26	29.03	34.47	39.19	42.95	45.7	47.6	48.7
Prob	5.62	5.77	5.44	4.72	3.76	2.75	1.9	1.1

This table contains the same errors as before. It is sensible to give less detail in this second table as the calculations are of the same type as those in the first table.

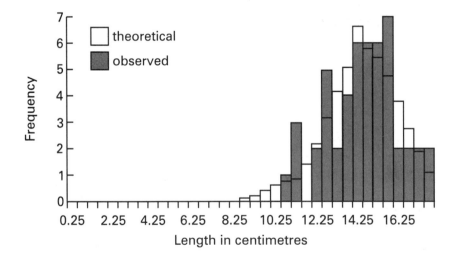

The horizontal scale for this graph of Y data is different from the scale on the graph of X data. This is acceptable as there is no need to compare the X, Y and Z distributions. Drawing histograms for expected and observed frequencies on the same axes makes comparison easy. Again, there are some errors.

Midpoint	2.75	3.25	3.75	4.25	4.75	5.25	5.75
Frequency	1	0	0	0	1	1	2
Probability	0.09	0.2	0.5	0.7	1.1	1.6	2.2

Midpoint	6.25	6.75	7.25	7.75	8.25	8.75	9.25
Frequency	5	1	2	3	6	5	5
Probability	2.9	3.5	4	4.7	4.7	4.7	4.3

Less detail given, which is sensible. The same errors are repeated.

Midpoint	9.75	10.25	10.75	11.25	11.75	12.25	12.75
Frequency	8	1	1	3	2	2	1
Probability	3.8	3.2	3.2	2.4	1.9	1.2	0 .9

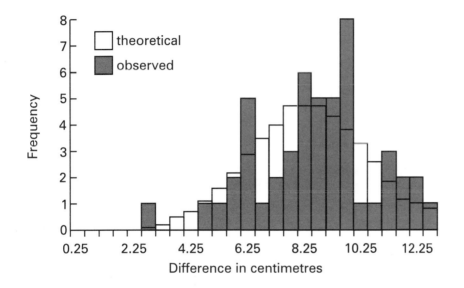

The graphs in this report were all produced from a computer package. This is desirable but lack of control of the program has resulted in unsatisfactory numbering of the horizontal axis. There are some errors.

Conclusions:

The sample has been drawn from pupils at my school. The pupils were not randomly sampled and therefore most subjects were either in the sixth form or certain other classes. This may have introduced bias as pupils of a certain age group or group of friends are able to judge the lengths given more accurately. This is fairly unlikely as the ability to judge is fairly even. However, to eliminate this bias pupils should have been sampled from all age groups so the results are as representative of the pupils as possible.

The data for estimating the 7 cm length fits a Normal model fairly well, rising to a peak and then falling. The data for estimating the 17 cm length also fits well. However, the data for estimating the difference does not fit so accurately although it still appears to fit fairly well as it does generally rise to a peak and then fall away.

The mean of the Z data should equal the mean of the Y data minus the mean of the X data.

$$\bar{z} = \bar{y} - \bar{x}$$

where
$\bar{z}$ = mean of the difference
$\bar{y}$ = mean of 17 cm estimate
$\bar{x}$ = mean of 7 cm estimate

The population seems to be defined as 'pupils from my school'. However, this has not been made very clear.

Good discussion of sampling and possible bias.

The X and Y variables are independent. If this is the case, then $X \pm Y \sim N(\mu_x \pm \mu_y, \sigma_x^2 + \sigma_y^2)$.

Therefore the mean of Z should equal $\mu_y - \mu_x$ and the standard deviation of Y squared plus the standard deviation of X squared should equal the standard deviation of Z squared.

$$\mu_z = \mu_y - \mu_x \qquad \sigma_z^2 = \sigma_y^2 + \sigma_x^2$$

$$8.6 = 14.4 - 5.8 \qquad 2.1^2 = 4.41$$

$$1.72^2 + 1.41^2 = 4.9$$

4.41 and 4.9 are fairly similar and therefore the standard deviation values confirm that the two distributions are independent (largely). The difference is probably due to the fact that 50 samples were taken and the subjects were not sampled completely randomly. For example, I sampled 1 group of 6th formers and 1 group of second years, and if certain groups carried out the estimate for 7 cm and 17 cm on the same lines then the distributions may not have been completely random. To improve this, more regularity could have been introduced into the method of taking samples.

If two distributions are completely random then when they are combined they should fit the distribution of the two combined named distributions. The standard deviations of these distributions confirm this fact but the graph for the combined distributions shows a poor fit and therefore does not support this theory *very well*. However, this is probably due to the fact that the variables do not fit a Normal distribution perfectly, may not be completely independent and are only taken from 50 samples, rather than the fact that the theory is incorrect.

Good discussion of independence and its implication for the mean and variance of Z.

The student does not have the population parameters (μ, σ^2). She has not made it clear that she is using estimates based on her sample. (See the first page of this report.) Details of the calculations are not given. This is acceptable at this level.

Good discussion as to why the observed data fails to perform exactly as the theory predicts.

14.5 Is a foot a foot long?

Data collection:

15 adult male subjects were asked, each subject was measured with shoes on and then with shoes off. The data was then arranged in a table.

Results:

This data is *matched pair data*.

	With shoes on – X	With shoes off – Y	Difference $X - Y$
1	28.5	26.0	2.5
2	28.5	24.0	4.5
3	30.5	27.0	3.5
4	28.5	26.0	2.5
5	31.0	27.9	3.1
6	28.0	25.4	2.6
7	28.0	26.4	1.6
8	30.7	26.9	3.8
9	30.0	27.1	2.9
10	29.6	27.5	2.1
11	26.2	22.0	4.2
12	28.0	26.8	1.2
13	32.0	29.7	2.3
14	30.2	28.2	2.0
15	28.2	25.8	2.4

Analysis:

With shoes on (X data)

Mean = 29.19
SD = 1.47
(Var = 2.17)
Best estimates = SD = 1.53
  Var = 2.34

With shoes off (Y data)

Mean = 26.45
SD = 1.74
(Var = 3.04)
Best estimates = SD = 1.81
  Var = 3.26

Confidence intervals

Using *t* tables:
95% confidence interval for the mean of X, μ_x = 28.35 to 30.04
95% confidence interval for the mean of Y, μ_y = 25.45 to 27.45

Conclusions:

The populations from which my sample is drawn is adult males. (The adult males are of a variety of ages and ethnic groups.)

Bias may have been introduced as some measurements were taken by myself and others by friends. I may have measured to a different degree of accuracy to my friends. Some measurements were taken when the subjects were standing and others where they were sitting, this may have introduced bias.

The confidence interval for 'X' (28.35, 30.04) does not contain the measurement 1 foot (30.48 cm). The confidence interval for 'Y' (25.45, 27.45) does not contain this measurement either.

Based on my results I can conclude that 'A foot is not a foot long'. (Perhaps when this measurement was made, people wore bigger shoes or perhaps boots!)

Extensions:

Confidence interval for the difference in foot length for 'shoes'/'without shoes'

95% confidence interval for the mean difference = 2.23 to 3.26

This shows that shoes are always bigger than feet.

Mean of the difference = 41.2/15 = 2.75

The use of '=' here is not ideal. (28.35, 30.04) would be better. This calculation assumes that the distribution is Normal. As we are dealing with the mean of a sample of 15 this is a perfectly reasonable assumption (by the Central Limit Theorem). This should have been mentioned.

She has considered possible biases in the method of measurement but not in the method of sampling.

Confidence intervals are for μ_x and μ_y, not X and Y.

Final conclusion answers the original question concisely and is based on the data collected. Excellent!

This is a light-hearted remark which is clearly true. However, the confidence interval does not show this: it shows that the mean of the difference between shoe length and foot length is greater than zero.

Note: Students unfamiliar with the t-distribution may use the z-distribution which will give a similar, but slightly narrower interval. The z-distribution assumes that σ is known exactly. This is not the case here, so the t-distribution is technically correct.

15 Notes on exercises

Chapter 1

1.1 Library books – simple random sampling
Expected outcome: Means of large samples cluster more closely around population mean than do the means of small samples.

1.2 Christmas club – comparison of different methods of sampling
Expected outcome: Means of subjective sample will not cluster about the population mean. Stratified sample means will cluster more closely than others. Means of large random samples will cluster more closely than means of small random samples. Cluster sample means will be biased and more variable than the others as the clusters are fairly homogeneous.

1.3 Volunteers – comparison of random and non-random methods of sampling
Expected outcome: Random sample will be more representative of population than the volunteers.

Chapter 2

2.1 Father's age at birth of subject – summarising data
Expected outcome: Distribution will have a positive skew. No compelling reason for choosing any particular diagram or summary statistics.

2.2 Greek puzzle – summarising data
Expected outcome: Construction of frequency distribution possible as last class is '$x >$' but exact values are not all known (truncated distribution). Any diagrams require assumptions (guesses) to be made. Cumulative frequency curve needs fewest assumptions but is not necessarily the best. Median, mode and interquartile range may be calculated exactly but other numerical measures need assumptions about the upper class bound.

2.3 Journey times – comparing two samples, outliers probable
Expected outcome: No compelling reason to choose any particular numerical measures or diagrams.

2.4 Parliamentary elections – comparing distributions
Expected outcome: Bar chart effective for seeing which candidate got most votes in the by-election. Pie charts effectively illustrate contrast between proportion of votes and seats won by the major parties. Pie charts also effective for comparing numbers of votes cast in Scotland and in the UK.

2.5 Churchyard – comparison of two samples with substantially different shapes and parameters
Expected outcome: No compelling reason to choose any particular numerical measure or diagram.

2.6 Apples – exploratory analysis of data using facilities of a statistical computer package
Expected outcome: For apples A and B there is negative correlation between quantity and price. Apple C is overall the most expensive and quantity is not related to price.

Chapter 3

3.1 Satellite TV – relative frequency
Expected outcome: As n increases the relative frequency will approach a constant value.

3.2 Pedestrian controlled crossing – conditional probability
Expected outcome: Demonstrating laws of probability.

3.3 Random numbers – comparison of patterns in random number tables with patterns predicted from probability theory
Expected outcome: Good agreement between observed and theoretical patterns.

Chapter 4

4.1 Darts – Binomial distribution
Expected outcome: Binomial model adequate unless data is affected by tiredness/boredom or the subject improves with practice.

4.2 Weighted container – Binomial distribution
Expected outcome: Binomial model adequate.

4.3 Number recall – Binomial distributions
Expected outcome: Binomial model adequate for both sets of data. P(incorrect) is smaller when the number is read as two blocks of 4 digits.

4.4 Electoral register – dependent versus independent trials
Expected outcome: Binomial model will not be an adequate model when all names on the register are included since it is likely that voters at the same address will have the same surname – the trials will not be independent. Binomial model likely to provide an adequate model when only one name per address included.

4.5 Multiple choice quiz – Binomial distribution with constant probability
Expected outcome: Binomial model will provide an adequate model for correct guesses but not for correct answers since some questions will be easier than others – probability of success will not be constant.

Chapter 5

5.1 Personal column – Poisson distribution
Expected outcome: Poisson model likely to be adequate for local weekly paper but not for national papers. Students will find population difficult to define.

5.2 Spot the difference quiz – Poisson distribution
Expected outcome: Poisson model probably adequate.

5.3 Pedestrian crossing – sum of two Poisson distributions
Expected outcome: Poisson model adequate for
 (i) the number of people arriving singly
 (ii) the number of groups arriving (NB not the number of people arriving in groups) and
 (iii) the sum of these two distributions with mean $(\overline{x} + \overline{y})$.

5.4 Supermarket – Poisson distribution, constant mean
Expected outcome: Poisson model adequate for both distributions but not for the combined distribution since for this distribution the mean is not constant.

5.5 Arrivals and departures – Poisson distribution, independent events
Expected outcome: Poisson distribution adequate for arrivals but not for departures, since departures will not be independent – many people alight from a single train.

Chapter 6

6.1 Guessing heights – Normal model
Expected outcome: Normal distribution will be an adequate model.

6.2 Weights – distribution of independent random variables
Expected outcome: Normal model adequate for all variables.
Means of bottles + mean of contents = mean of full bottles.
Variance of bottles + variance of contents ≈ variance of full bottles since weight of bottle and contents are independent.

6.3 Estimating length – distribution of difference of independent events
Expected outcome: Normal model adequate for all variables.
$\overline{x} - \overline{y} = \overline{d}$
$s_x^2 + s_y^2 \approx s_d^2$
since X and Y are independent.

6.4 Dice – distribution of sample mean
Expected outcome: Good agreement between observed relative frequency and probability. Central Limit Theorem demonstrated.

6.5 Pennies – Normal distribution
Expected outcome: Normal model adequate, counting pennies by weight unlikely to lead to error.

Chapter 7

7.1 Ear lobes – confidence interval for proportions
Expected outcome: Increasing sample size reduces the width of the confidence interval.

7.2 Reading glasses – confidence intervals for proportions
Expected outcome: Bigger proportion of older age group require reading glasses.

7.3 Is a foot a foot long? – confidence interval for the mean
Expected outcome: On average male feet are not a foot long.

7.4 Random Normal variables I – confidence interval for the mean, σ known
Expected outcome: Observed percentage of intervals containing the mean is approximately equal to the percentage associated with the confidence interval. Increasing the sample size decreases the width of the interval.

7.5 Random Normal variables II – confidence interval for mean, σ unknown
Expected outcome: When t is used the percentage of intervals containing the mean is approximately the same as the percentage confidence. If z is used with samples of size 3, too few intervals contain the mean. With samples of size 20 there is little difference between using t and using z.

In Chapters 8, 9, 11 and 12 most of the exercises consist of carrying out a hypothesis test and interpreting the results. The outcome will depend on the exact circumstances of the test and students should not be too concerned if the 'expected outcome' does not occur.

In Chapter 10 the exercises consist largely of examining whether two variables are linearly related and commenting on the strength of any such relationship. Again, the 'expected outcome' may not occur.

Chapter 8

8.1 Vital statistics – hypothesis test for mean, σ known
Expected outcome: Unpredictable, will depend on how the sample is chosen.

8.2 Kids – hypothesis test for proportion
Expected outcome: Hypothesis likely to be accepted.

8.3 Letters – hypothesis test for mean of a Poisson distribution
Expected outcome: Poisson model adequate, difference unlikely to be established if only one or two days' post is used, but may show up if 10 days' post is used.

8.4 Puzzles – hypothesis test for means using paired t-test
Expected outcome: Will depend on the choice of puzzles, but it is likely that a difference will be found.

8.5 Tower of Hanoi – F-test and comparison of means
Expected outcome: Will depend on the choice of groups but it is likely that significant differences will be found.

8.6 Random Normal variables III – hypothesis test for means, type I and type II error
Expected outcome: If H_0 is true the percentage of times it is rejected will be approximately the same as the significance level of the test. If H_0 is not true *(i)* increasing the significance level decreases the proportion of type II errors and *(ii)* increasing the sample size decreases the proportion of type II errors.

8.7 Weighing – test for mean, σ unknown
Expected outcome: Sample mean unlikely to agree with the actual weight unless the weighing machine has been calibrated recently.

8.8 Precision of measurements – F-test
Expected outcome: Less variability likely with ruler but samples may not be large enough for the difference to be significant.

Chapter 9

9.1 Jigsaws – one-factor analysis of variance
Expected outcome: Difference between puzzles – plain puzzles take longer.

9.2 Above/below – two-factor analysis of variance
Expected outcome: Difference between % false screens.

9.3 Sorting – two-factor analysis of variance
Expected outcome: Likely to be differences between subjects. First sort will probably be the slowest but difference may not be sufficient to be detected by analysis of variance.

9.4 Volume – one-factor analysis of variance
Expected outcome: Depends on relative accuracy of instruments used.

Chapter 10

10.1 Clothes – rank correlation
Expected outcome: Positive but fairly small correlation.

10.2 Estimating age I – regression
Expected outcome: Strong, approximately linear relationship. Residuals may have a tendency to increase with age of person in photograph.

10.3 Germinating peas – product–moment correlation coefficient
Expected outcome: Positive correlation.

10.4 Pulse rate in exercise – regression, interpretation of coefficients
Expected outcome: heart rate increases with the number of step-ups, but the relationship may not be linear.

10.5 Estimating age II – regression, repeated observations
Expected outcome: Clear indication of linear relationship between mean estimated age and actual age. May be some tendency for standard deviation of estimates to increase with age of person in photograph.

10.6 Tennis player – speed of serve – regression, comparison of different explanatory variables
Expected outcome: The speed of serve may be related to height and weight but not age.

Chapter 11

11.1 School absences – goodness of fit to Uniform distribution
Expected outcome: Absences not independent of the day of the week.

11.2 Digits of π – goodness of fit, Geometric distribution
Expected outcome: Model is adequate.

11.3 Churches – goodness of fit, Exponential distribution
Expected outcome: Model is adequate.

11.4 Supermarket receipts – 3×3 contingency table
Expected outcome: Number of items may not be independent of the day of the week.

11.5 Colours – 4×2 contingency table
Expected outcome: The named colours are correctly identified more often.

Chapter 12

12.1 Pebbles – Mann Whitney U test
Expected outcome: Pebbles further up the beach are larger. Mann Whitney U test will probably show a significant difference.

12.2 End of year examination results – Wilcoxon signed rank test
Expected outcome: Unpredictable.

12.3 Arm wrestling – sign test
Expected outcome: Older group will win more contests than younger group but sample may not be large enough for sign test to show a significant difference.

12.4 Random Normal variables IV – comparison of sign test, Wilcoxon signed rank test and paired t-test applied to matched pairs from a Normal distribution
Expected outcome: A – all tests reject the (true) null hypothesis about 20 times out of 100.

B – the (false) null hypothesis is rejected most often by the t-test, followed by Wilcoxon signed rank test, followed by the sign test. All tests reject more than 20 times out of 100.

12.5 Births and deaths – sign test
Expected outcome: More '+' than '−'. There may not be enough data for the sign test to show a significant difference.

12.6 Shopping basket – comparison of sign test, Wilcoxon signed rank test and paired t-test for matching pairs
Expected outcome: Wilcoxon and t-test likely to show supermarket prices lower but there may not be enough data for the sign test to detect this difference.

Chapter 13

13.1 Simulated data I – control charts
for attributes
Expected outcome: About one sample in 40 from P will be above the upper warning limit and one in 40 below the lower warning limit. An increase in proportion signalled for samples from Q.

13.2 Simulated data II – control charts
for means and standard deviations
Expected outcome: For each chart only about 1 point in 20 will be outside the warning limits for samples from A. For samples from B action is likely to be signalled on the means chart, but not on the standard deviation chart. For samples from C, action is likely to be signalled on the standard deviation chart and possibly on the means chart.

13.3 Compact discs – control charts for
means and standard deviations
Expected outcome: The mean will be too high for the first 10 samples, then brought under control. Variability increases at samples 17 and 18 and then is brought under control.

13.4 Packets of crisps I – acceptance
sampling by attributes
Expected outcome: It is likely that the batch will be accepted.

13.5 Packets of crisps II – acceptance
sampling by variable
Expected outcome: It is likely that the batch will be accepted.

13.6 Simulated data III – double sampling
(plan from BS 6001)
Expected outcome: For $p = 0.025$ the batch will nearly always be accepted – a second sample will be required about 4 times out of 10. For $p = 0.1$ the batch will be accepted about 4 times out of 10 – a second sample will be required about 5 times out of 10. For $p = 0.01$ the batch will always be accepted – a second sample will be required about 2 times out of 10.

13.7 Re–formed scampi – acceptance
sampling defining non-conforming packets
Expected outcome: non-conforming defined as containing less than about 452.5 g. Take a sample of 25 and reject batch if the sample contains 9 or more non-conforming.
Batch 2 will usually be rejected as the mean is too low.
Batch 3 will be accepted because the mean is high.
Batch 4 will usually be rejected because of high variability.

Appendix

Table 1 N(20, 4²)

24.44	25.74	19.57	21.47	14.21	23.58	16.17	26.57	19.38	22.42	16.12	12.96	16.75	18.48	16.44	21.76	18.05	23.39	17.36	21.95	23.75	26.12
14.25	15.35	28.95	25.23	25.82	20.94	19.91	21.27	25.92	24.87	15.22	19.7	20.41	13.38	22.71	17.31	22.37	20.23	16.3	22.13	19.35	25.67
21.22	15.77	21.91	19.28	28.47	20.96	23.32	25.73	20.51	17.65	21.29	18.82	16.8	20.5	16.02	22.46	20.36	14.95	22.93	20.87	20.89	14.61
22.52	18.22	19.25	20.97	21.86	18.43	19.85	25.01	20.16	17.95	16.25	19.27	20.44	19.39	21.33	19.48	15.63	25.21	18.41	22.2	20.62	27.93
16.68	18.58	20.08	29.34	30.12	18.55	14.98	19.04	22.66	18.2	15.96	19.63	23.69	18.48	16.07	17.2	19.62	19.52	15.21	22.1	28.01	11.57
16.78	19.11	22.33	13.84	23.2	17.63	23.79	27.01	25.83	28.37	21.7	22.07	19.5	26.88	21.55	13.76	16.98	22.48	18.07	21.69	23.35	18.01
16.03	17.81	26.93	18.58	21.74	22.86	18.72	23.49	22.51	25.29	17.38	16.08	22.2	18.32	29.07	23.23	12.87	13.06	24.54	19.13	16.09	18.7
14.44	16.26	22.51	22.73	16.26	14.21	18.24	24.71	14.92	19.27	15.08	17.81	18.64	18.67	20.93	17.42	22.09	22.56	27.32	20.02	18.48	21.63
21.32	22.14	15.34	16.92	19.79	16.86	10.63	20.79	28.09	20.46	20.43	20.14	16.69	13.37	25.04	21.67	20.07	10.86	25.66	16.61	15.41	18.5
17.9	27.21	18.12	21.23	25.47	20.55	12.63	16.52	22.35	20.59	19.03	27.5	15.74	21.06	16.92	21.06	19.49	18	24.44	21.83	18.58	21.14
22.41	23.47	23.22	25.88	19.45	25.6	16.51	22.15	24.39	26.72	14.82	17.8	18.49	23.32	16.79	15.01	15.53	9.29	17.24	20.95	23.01	19.5
23.66	21	21.98	18.9	21.68	17.11	15.36	19.47	23.27	21.14	22.02	29.05	16.89	20.73	23.11	16.04	19.35	15.97	25.39	15.68	19.35	20.42
16.71	14.76	18.85	22.22	21.53	18.77	20.56	24.02	15.86	17.57	24.87	23.03	17.36	16.98	18.81	9.65	24.05	20.12	13.47	18.39	17.2	14.35
18.11	24.12	21.41	19.41	26.28	23.48	20.61	21.66	19.17	23.49	19.67	17.77	23.03	15	17.46	19.52	22.99	20.88	16.39	17.85	18.31	13.49
21.87	12.89	12.09	22.9	15.77	19.6	14.39	21.87	22.16	23.93	17.48	21.34	30.43	20.44	23.42	27.49	16.16	23.54	26.35	24.09	19.28	17.94
19.05	20.06	13.54	21.95	21.04	18.69	16.45	17.39	20.62	28.95	18.58	15.83	20.62	18.99	21.61	12.66	24.29	18.22	20.25	16.99	20.06	17.64
27.15	22.2	19.83	24.43	22.78	22.29	21.52	19.48	21.95	19.73	15.57	20.88	20.06	22.37	22.06	19.82	16.82	19.79	19.75	21.38	13.46	16.71
19.51	14.4	16	21.38	18.37	16.66	23.29	21.09	21.87	19.62	22.14	18.06	19.02	26.07	20.97	18.59	26.26	15.1	18.51	15.57	12.83	19.51
17.62	26.88	22.32	18.07	22.73	22.16	18.48	17.28	16.02	15.73	18.53	16.08	12.61	21.47	22.34	15.01	21.78	23.47	17.53	14.13	25.92	16.38
16.31	27.89	22.02	17.83	18.02	21.47	18.08	17.96	24.51	11.53	19.01	25.22	14.95	15.57	16.58	19.4	19.73	21.99	18.91	22.92	22.23	16.53
23.33	18.12	18.97	17.17	20.18	23.88	19.6	18.98	24.51	19.82	16.48	17.34	16.77	23.84	21.42	26.04	11.55	25.77	17.29	14.62	12.29	25.35
22.99	21.02	18.52	19.96	26.93	22.21	16.06	25.57	21.74	18.21	17.36	21.85	21.37	18.77	17.67	27.69	18.05	25.21	26.36	18.92	13.9	23.51
16.26	22.2	21.2	22.47	21.99	13.11	18.95	20.35	21.97	19.96	19.32	17.25	18.2	17.53	25.28	13.26	17.47	15.75	24.67	20.56	18	19.39
13.52	20.33	22.18	17.49	23.77	22.34	22.71	19.13	17.02	17.91	15.02	24.55	20.75	17.79	12.12	16.69	16.53	19.01	21.26	20.91	17.86	16.68
24.87	20.17	18.76	20.42	24.63	15.77	21.9	16.94	13.92	16.8	23.8	17.82	23.14	26.7	28.36	22.59	26.83	12.85	20.15	22.7	19.56	19.27
24.78	17.31	20.74	17.15	25.62	13.26	24.06	9.14	20.24	16.8	17.1	22.8	24.17	24.61	25.11	21.62	23.38	27.41	20.64	11.24	29.83	18.25
11.9	26.58	9.97	22.41	27.28	15.25	10.72	16.78	22.63	21.1	14.8	17.89	25.15	21.05	28.46	23.97	25.76	20.79	22.08	16.4	13.41	8.82
17.84	15.05	17.17	15.25	14.21	16.62	25.25	20.65	18.66	21.64	15.24	27.76	13.85	19.51	17.4	21.71	21.28	19.55	22.49	14.21	22.44	12.02
13.58	20.27	23.7	22.86	22.11	14.89	21.61	17.31	15.58	14.8	16.92	21.38	10.27	32.09	15.26	23.66	20.95	18.29	12.53	18.18	17.22	24.81
25.54	26.48	23.95	19.2	22.15	18.08	17.52	22.94	20.59	19.32	21.51	21.6	16.36	15.35	18.34	20.28	15.23	17.09	14.66	20.94	22.25	17.3
22.78	20.73	26.72	19.39	22.84	18.04	24.57	21.6	18.26	16.79	18.56	23	20.59	16	21.37	19.98	17.31	21.35	17.43	13.75	20.92	31.51
17.99	18.8	26.07	21.31	13.13	18.51	15.84	20.08	16.77	23.91	12.74	23.68	20.83	14.18	23.09	18.96	23.99	19.67	14.08	22.53	25.04	24
23.06	10.48	11.29	22.25	24.52	20.65	21.46	20.73	11.49	21.07	18.33	15.42	13.24	11.8	17.05	20.03	19.18	22.78	13.11	18.2	21.33	12.63
23.68	19.62	28.13	23.78	21.52	17.22	23.64	18.95	19.14	18.47	18.73	19.16	21.22	11.11	17.59	23.61	20.3	17.31	14.72	22.79	21.93	24.29
21.35	19.61	23.45	15.11	26.41	26.57	20.9	10.13	10.73	15.39	19.56	21.2	19.87	20.95	18.89	22.39	22.52	18.67	20.77	17.2	13.21	27
20.47	21.5	25.73	24.23	19.68	25.13	18.29	20.28	18.09	25	26.92	19.2	23.76	27.43	21.36	24.87	13.59	19.16	19.41	20.01	16.76	16.91
19.66	25.71	17.3	18.45	17.55	20.1	17.98	22.35	17.36	18.69	13.74	24.53	13.55	27.84	14.27	16.59	16.56	23.93	19.83	18.9	23.37	28.39
6.66	13.87	21.38	15.29	20.52	18.16	20.06	21.9	21.34	17.02	21.23	15.64	21.17	20.6	25.49	17.42	20.66	13.64	12.71	22.49	23.59	17.17
14.09	22.52	16.59	12.86	18.57	23.7	29	17.03	17.89	23	20.61	26.81	24.4	17	18.48	25.22	26.07	17.03	15.49	21.04	19.3	10.62
19.73	25.94	25.94	19.64	15.35	17.98	18.31	17.89	23.87	15.82	19.09	24.4	20.28	18.99	20.3	19.93	16.63	22.43	23.49	22.78	22.6	15.72
25.25	18.07	22.77	21	23.67	20.55	27.65	23	20.02	20.85	16.37	17	18.48	20.05	15.03	23.15	20.32	12.25	22.78	21.12	17.76	18.35
17.44	14.77	13.31	16.68	20.29	23.78	24.46	17.86	19.6	29.4	21.39	15.67	25.22	13.24	20.05	18.29	28.1	22.04	18.72	17.64	16.88	20

(continued on next page)

Table 1 (continued)

23.62	18.76	23.37	28.71	20.34	20.04	23.16	20.98	22.76	19.7	18.61	22.43	24.49	25.06	17.2	18.76	19.57	17.67	17.99	26.68	15.03	22.55	24.27	23.32
18.42	26.57	22.15	14.05	22.44	25.93	13.53	16.98	27.43	18.81	12.98	20.87	21.85	14.82	16.55	21.22	16.82	18.63	19.09	29.47	22.62	21.36	13.81	19.71
20.98	16.35	25.91	18.79	21.09	14.21	17.49	22.25	15.96	29.04	10.45	22.85	9.83	21.97	25.4	21.15	18.83	24.54	18.8	20.17	20.66	18.71	18.7	23.64
16.29	23.67	24.34	23.09	15.7	14.47	19.11	27.26	15.05	22.16	11.67	17.25	14.43	15.87	26.36	22.06	25.16	20.28	27.03	18.09	23.25	25.05	26.76	23.21
12.29	17.97	17.18	30.03	15.76	17.31	16.91	14.99	21.92	16.43	14.97	19.33	17.44	22.31	20.42	21.28	24.69	20.13	19.22	19.69	19.98	28.52	21.05	21.63
18.84	19.22	20.85	22.35	16.75	11.47	16.15	23.92	24.58	21.38	21.18	24.94	27.7	19.14	13.79	10.82	10.7	19.74	15.12	16.01	22.85	25.88	24.03	18
18.52	24.81	14.08	12.76	16.57	23.4	22.9	19.76	17.82	23.53	19.61	23.13	24.68	8.8	21.12	19.48	28.01	20.83	16.55	20	20.42	20.17	22.36	31.24
19.96	14.63	21.31	25.86	16.18	17.05	16.25	24.86	15.11	16.68	20.74	19.37	21.65	10.32	22.4	22.56	20.22	19.87	21.74	17.08	25.19	20.45	26.13	28.29
21.95	19.45	20.7	24.22	14.32	25.59	19.56	23.25	14.39	14.74	16.55	17.51	21.52	27.18	24.73	18.48	23.36	23.5	23.14	20.83	25.78	25.77	10.66	17.37
23.59	21.63	21.02	17.7	20.64	15.4	25.47	19.8	22.75	20.63	21.17	17.36	21.59	16.6	21.73	19.17	18.52	24.07	14.75	20.7	24.92	23.14	17.52	18.27
20.21	13.61	17.85	26.54	23.34	21.46	25.61	18.28	20.15	27.6	19.62	24.89	21.61	11.39	19.99	15.36	17.84	28.09	19.95	21.59	19.34	13.82	11.44	21.25
18.06	19.86	13.78	14.27	18.85	17.17	26.97	14.23	19.4	23.34	17.64	19.17	22.47	18.52	23.05	24.27	22.31	21.99	18.97	15.9	22.64	26.02	22.54	16.08
19.57	16.2	7.74	22.34	22.61	26.2	16.22	22.32	14.16	12.09	23.62	19.88	21.57	19.91	27.36	30.4	23.29	26.57	18.56	16.89	26.12	20.29	17.77	16.55
19.71	23.24	21.37	11.15	20.75	11.55	25.19	19.52	18.73	16.24	15.82	18.02	21.2	16.68	21.26	22.49	15.74	14.8	23.47	19.34	21.29	24.85	14.61	21.44
20.08	27.39	18.44	20.25	18.37	18.74	20.08	22.47	21.21	25.44	17.68	23.57	17.69	16.35	22.03	24.29	24.57	11.99	18.03	16.65	23.59	20.22	16.52	18.6
11.72	18.02	24.39	17.98	16.08	23.54	25.39	13.3	28.27	20.52	23.64	18.82	21.46	18.66	21.27	12.83	20.14	21.59	17.4	16.23	17.72	19.8	17.59	21.22
15.4	13.96	23.26	26.41	23.16	21.17	20.46	27.96	24.29	19.83	18.51	18.1	25.28	13.12	23.91	20.13	17.69	23.8	20.33	15	22	20.79	23.65	21.56
23.27	25.78	24.6	22.11	23.04	20.75	23.57	20.3	22.65	15.39	18.99	22.71	17.2	23.04	17.88	22.47	25.07	25.98	19.75	21.7	23.66	21.97	18.01	17.5
20.69	19.92	14.84	21.36	21.17	23.21	23.91	24.52	13.17	24.84	24.82	17.89	15.04	14.16	23.76	22.89	22.23	16.86	14.64	20.49	16.48	21.99	19.99	17.99
21.26	20.63	23.03	18.36	21.71	19.09	24.07	24.75	22.08	22.42	18.57	13.45	22.46	19.53	18.76	18.42	19.86	17.2	22.05	24.81	12.57	22.85	25.36	21.39
16.47	23.98	16.58	18.76	18.76	30.4	20.62	18.01	14.04	23.71	18.03	16.3	22.84	16.44	20.29	17.79	13.18	13.58	23.34	15.61	21.56	20.09	21.37	17.14
20.01	21.47	23.52	16.62	18.62	23.46	29.36	12.51	17.59	22.71	23.78	16.51	19.88	20.49	21.33	18.03	15.33	21.57	17.8	19.34	18.51	21.35	22.66	15.79
16.12	17.69	18.46	21.36	21.36	21.56	18.19	24.19	23.93	23.89	19.75	15.92	13.59	20.16	13.98	29.39	13.88	19.58	15.63	17.79	19.8	19.52	21.25	23.28
24.05	18.56	21.56	25.36	24.87	18.14	17.91	18.53	11.67	11.67	24.57	21.15	18.92	22.87	24.35	19.56	14.23	20.36	25.58	16.2	13.19	20.38	24.06	16.18
15.13	22.32	14.08	23.12	18.61	24.58	20.27	26.34	24.24	23.63	14.65	24.62	29.16	23.01	23.25	19.8	26.33	15.42	15.68	13.58	22	23.71	26.36	19.18
15.84	26.56	18.06	15.44	23.01	28.78	22.29	23.2	19.84	11.96	19.09	14.87	21.12	15.78	18.08	27.23	18.46	22.09	18.3	21.38	26.27	19.57	21.92	22.51
13.07	24.54	16.47	19.25	26.46	16.92	13.15	15.07	14.89	23.24	22.13	21.59	19.51	22.26	21.6	13.38	19.24	12.79	20.45	22.58	20.83	17.49	16.37	17.87
20.52	12.28	27.12	17.58	21.42	21.87	19.87	17.41	15.45	12.01	19.51	27.44	13.52	21.38	15.7	19.65	23.72	23.58	22.91	24.92	19.85	14.93	24.62	26.19
23.2	19.74	22.16	20.05	11.2	16.77	27.92	14.36	26.05	16.43	23.8	22.03	22.98	28.47	17.94	17.63	27.13	25.74	18.27	20.75	23.46	18.39	23.22	19.02
19.76	21.53	24.67	20.01	19.94	23.45	15.85	17.2	17.82	22.82	18.03	17.59	22.12	15.59	19.31	27.11	15.23	20.61	22.07	19.69	19.14	21.05	18.73	18.37
22.8	12.8	20.14	22.13	25.34	20.47	18.69	15.56	10.97	22	25.97	17.59	24.14	18.77	13.91	14.47	14.19	24.1	16.34	18.41	21.94	19.41	24.99	18.02
19.64	15.21	23.45	19.37	18.69	25.28	24.01	23	20.64	14.48	14.18	20.69	19.87	18.3	19.08	20.63	24.96	18.74	17.15	16.46	20.6	14.59	23.63	20.36
13.49	24.72	18.22	27.31	20.17	22.59	19.94	17.13	18.43	18.09	24.07	17.21	12.76	18.91	16	18.1	20.64	16.72	26.26	16.79	23.83	21.23	21.09	19.42
25.11	22.5	13.26	24.53	16.79	23.7	11.21	24.65	20	13.42	19.93	23.55	17.87	22.58	24.33	23.56	12.23	7.77	26.13	21.59	18.64	19.28	20.01	14.31
21.47	17.2	21.91	20.14	23.64	21.09	22.47	20.93	19.18	22.76	16.85	18.3	20.02	12.49	23.35	17.03	23.13	17.14	16.42	27.56	20.82	13.03	12.35	12.04
27.04	13.5	13.66	15.23	21.56	25.99	29.12	22.54	32.27	16.3	20.27	24.03	27.3	24.28	19.28	21.54	20.5	15.69	17.35	22.07	17.58	11.28	18.36	8.42
14.71	27.49	14.81	19.77	23.24	22.16	24.39	16.94	20.75	21.6	14.38	16.95	24.4	8.04	13.2	18.23	20.76	19.29	17.93	18.74	23.6	19.78	17.61	19.83
20.76	24.93	22.48	19.45	24.24	21.57	23.32	25.93	16.4	18	15.65	21.21	16.47	14.65	20.96	19.55	17.34	16.9	17.09	22.84	16.65	19.55	26.26	22.07
21.76	16.7	21.46	19.69	28.7	20.7	23.37	16.49	22.57	19.07	16.3	29.03	21.51	19.11	22	28.49	27.59	16.95	16.86	26.91	15.12	12.8	23.05	15.6
26.68	18.06	23.93	13.64	25.68	20.33	14.95	23.16	22.07	13.2	18.23	26.56	17.12	17	29.32	22	16.44	20.69						
18.79	20.44	22.58	26.78	16.96	21.03	25.15	20.03	19.3	21.83	22.23	17.79	16.44	16.89	12.92	21.05	26.91	20.65						
19.41	25.46	18.09	16.11	14.68	13.47	20.1	30.98	19.76	25.04	23.27	19.7	16.44	16.89	23.86	19.7	20.69	19.19						

continued on next page

Table 2 N(23, 4²)

16.13	21.21	24.47	27.01	23.35	21.15	20.13	19.05	13.53	28.81	24.68	24.13	22.76	19.58	17.72	17.87	26	19.75	22.72	14.45	28.63	27.02	25.53	19.97
22.1	19.53	23.08	23.56	27.01	20.13	19.4	26.47	21.89	26.82	17.61	21.35	23.06	26.33	20.42	19.73	26.29	16.86	26.16	21.52	21.4	18.29	24.81	17.49
24.5	22.51	22.12	26.03	22.27	22.35	24.26	18.85	32.04	15.47	26.57	17.16	19.63	27.11	16.61	20.34	28.74	23.35	24.88	16.85	24.87	13.44	27.82	20.49
13.12	22.78	25.14	22.88	31.12	29.36	25.46	21.96	25.78	24.99	24.62	22.05	22.94	20.7	23.93	15.63	22.38	24.8	28.82	14.14	28.12	29.15	15.19	17.53
27.3	26.09	18.77	29.31	18.19	22.79	26.81	18.08	20.49	28.21	26.94	20.03	15.61	22.89	20.76	26.81	26.51	23.88	17.19	36.06	20.76	32.36	22.26	24.65
25.65	27.21	20.36	16.37	15.91	23.55	27.96	24.26	20.42	19.39	14.72	18.73	26.37	21.18	28.06	26.81	20.98	17.89	27.24	24.24	13.87	15.9	23.57	26.24
25	22.89	27.08	22.69	20.9	28.57	25.81	26	18.11	30.55	20.97	16.55	21.77	21.18	27.79	26	25.61	30.77	26.58	23.73	20.46	21.72	24.25	19.51
20.43	19.98	24.61	26.02	17.99	23.72	19.46	19.65	22.1	24.88	22.01	22.83	23.59	19.94	19.66	21.16	18.48	18.96	23	22.12	21.38	25.02	20.49	15.48
25.88	25.71	21.01	19.83	24.72	24.33	24.51	29.67	17.92	26.65	16.2	23.28	24.47	28.74	28.6	23.51	20.88	22.6	25.25	26.89	27.63	21.51	27.41	22.33
29.7	24.62	26.45	21.03	22.91	15.47	23.84	25.89	24.14	23.2	27.97	25.75	15.87	27.01	23.48	15.53	17.68	22.27	26.31	20.58	29.81	20.87	20.55	13.49
19.45	24.99	18.96	16.71	26.23	23.11	23.25	25.58	29.71	24.95	26.88	18.04	21.97	19.22	28.44	24.23	26.17	26.98	30.99	27.89	25.61	26.24	21.01	22.98
16.74	23.17	14.68	21.41	18.55	22.1	27.86	22.89	17.32	25.81	26.17	18.75	26.16	22.55	22.51	19.22	26.9	23.14	26.42	20.56	21.15	19.65	18.58	26.82
24.26	25.83	24.87	21.88	29.51	21.5	17.17	25.53	21.99	26.45	23.69	24.27	27.44	29.57	24.56	25.24	19.63	23.33	23.64	29.49	32.78	25.25	19.1	11.28
21.7	15.55	25.67	22.32	23.79	22.98	24.95	24.49	27.54	22.94	23.51	25.8	16.65	26.11	19.63	19.28	21.41	23.05	23.01	31.43	14.84	19.74	17.61	24.77
24.84	20.33	21.79	24.77	23.62	33.15	17.86	26.38	17.23	21.27	24.14	18.58	19.98	17.69	33.86	23.8	20.32	30.7	34.08	22.94	25.33	17.87	21.53	20.3
23.77	19.02	28.97	22.43	22.67	29.17	13.68	25.27	24.22	25.54	24.33	19.08	27.83	23.19	25.55	21.97	19.4	24.79	24.83	23.38	28.62	25.2	16.51	20.86
19.82	26.33	20.75	20.86	22.97	21.21	26.91	24.49	26.75	20.16	27.51	23.24	18.9	21.28	29.5	22.57	20.5	28.63	23.23	28.64	24.15	17.88	24.93	22.09
25.97	27.23	21.9	20.45	16.82	25.07	18.35	18.23	26.51	24.52	22.5	24.39	24.64	19.83	20.87	22.01	22.07	28.69	22.88	29.71	23.56	24.43	33.13	19.61
20.63	23.94	27.02	14.5	27.02	26.32	27.52	28	28.59	22.09	21.29	17.69	23.04	26.14	24.76	22.08	20.4	26.18	28.01	20.05	23.23	24.11	29.56	26.72
19.72	22.24	22.31	24.36	24.23	22.15	26.05	23.27	28.79	23.35	21.59	27.94	26.41	19.2	22.44	25.35	25.09	18.47	26.45	19.4	26.37	27.15	20.6	23.54
21.19	22.5	14.71	17.19	23.54	20.22	22.8	23.43	18.71	24.95	14.28	25.11	23.53	17.99	23.28	24.72	26.79	24.88	23.29	26.79	25.13	14.28	27.83	25.09
23.88	31.46	18.54	21.99	27.86	24.91	23.24	16.87	24.31	25.25	16.44	21.68	22.8	19.97	21.05	21.22	22.26	17.76	16.97	19.1	18.59	23.01	21.66	26.47
25.97	24.79	30.26	21.99	21.61	33.42	17.63	25.51	18.68	21.53	23.3	24.31	18.43	20.67	22.21	22.18	16.63	15.59	27.12	21.66	20.38	17.76	20.29	25.33
21.34	21.79	21.47	16.11	27.64	17.79	30.93	20.12	21.54	26.76	25.64	21	27.53	27.12	22.24	17.3	20.39	23.89	27.97	21.94	16.94	22.22	16.8	14.74
25.35	25.12	27.36	26.98	21.16	27.09	17.69	25.89	19.16	21	15.81	28.09	22.57	25.75	27.22	22.84	19.94	23.67	28.26	15.53	22.79	26.91	13.12	20.87
14.78	27.44	28.86	25.18	23.51	21.76	27.62	28.67	29.34	22.95	20.8	18.4	20.69	25.03	19.8	25.19	22.05	21.44	19.6	19.77	30.46	19.77	23.17	24.79
14.52	22.31	20.18	29.05	18.83	24.53	16.22	25.3	21.5	25.3	29.73	24.59	17.8	24.89	25.91	22.27	21.44	25.76	22.47	18.95	22.47	17.15	23.8	25.73
26.38	27.35	23.68	21.28	17.96	25.72	20.68	24.15	17.77	31.87	18.31	30.64	33.39	18.11	21.01	22.19	20.96	20.45	28.03	17.56	24	25.61	23.44	22.46
24.26	25.59	21.05	29.98	18.35	24.01	16.82	27.1	18.34	20.05	24.82	25.61	18.18	19.77	23.97	15.53	18.68	21.31	24.92	24.84	20.44	16.21	21.46	21.71
21.07	24.08	18.97	20.38	20.45	29.32	23.03	17.25	21.59	22.19	27.39	23.56	28.7	27.02	18.98	25.45	22.33	23.55	21.51	27.3	8.02	25.5	21.76	22.39
27.71	21.6	24.03	24.2	23.78	24.29	22.03	27.36	19.45	21.62	26.91	20.37	24.22	18.02	22.09	28.33	25.58	18.67	22.07	13.89	15.57	21.64	28.79	27.5
25.28	21.64	21.4	23.31	24.62	24.26	22.01	24.85	19.23	24.67	23.59	25.64	22.53	28.88	33.94	17.96	25.66	18.64	21.61	25.99	17.47	23.24	15.98	14.67
32.27	36.35	17.86	20.96	19.21	21.81	19.26	19.1	22.24	20.05	25.26	31.12	16.18	28.18	27.18	25.66	24.47	24.27	24.6	19.79	16.63	18.79	26.13	19.2
20.48	18.45	20.87	23.83	14.84	17.52	23.71	30.7	23.84	27.1	17.31	18.85	21.13	25.38	18.06	22.31	25.96	24.13	22.13	25.14	17.02	27.27	33.15	23.01
24.48	19.52	29	18.98	22.43	30.7	16.38	24.47	22.7	25.58	25.85	16.18	25.35	23.34	23.44	23.87	26.43	25.17	21.33	22.49	24.56	18.72	23.3	20.77
20.51	10.48	27.82	24.33	18.33	24.48	27.16	19.1	18.11	30.86	18.52	19.98	26.83	22.77	31.72	22.2	24.26	14.68	20.86	18.28	27.22	28.01	23.44	18.83
14.95	24.99	21.6	21.6	23.07	23.65	18.99	22.12	22.19	27.61	11.82	25.76	22.19	20.39	17.63	18.57	22.88	22.04	25.18	22.35	27.54	24.49	21.21	20.91
20.06	22.36	23.04	31.53	21.74	31.44	23.2	15.52	26.38	19.83	27.82	23.04	25.27	20.39	18.7	23.04	23.08	22.3	27.51	19.67	21.84	22.96	25.19	26.03
24.04	16.13	19.89	30.67	16.45	22.42	19.98	27.49	33.08	20.93	20.41	19.82	17.41	27.74	22.71	25.35	20.04	24.23	22	20.84	22.87	25.82	21.99	20.41
25.31	13.97	28.5	26.96	26.66	24.51	19.22	27.49	24.57	21.25	17.77	23.16	26.04	20.29	27.77	26.15	22.5	24.12	22	24.99	24.47	24.99	22.87	28.99
22.03	22.33	23.42	24.42	23.9	28.6	22.63	22.12	14.15	20.06	21.67	19.81	20.32	20.24	24.62	25.12	23.11	24.13	21.17	20.84	27.54	24.47	16.86	27.11
20.21	20.85	18.92	14.89	22.27	17.99	20.7	22.64	28.97	21.7	20.37	16.42	27.2	30.8	25.05	23.11	20.56	20.91	16.82	24.53	21.84	26.47	18.09	29.65

(continued on next page)

Table 2 (continued)

23.43	23.44	24.21	25.82	23.21	18.21	18	18.22	22.12	21.75	25.83	27.56
18.91	17.74	27.3	22.21	23.31	20.77	27.93	22.53	26.49	23.83	27.53	23.41
17.54	20.5	22.27	26.41	27.42	30.05	19.9	20.24	26.25	26.4	26.89	30.99
17.06	21.8	25.2	24.63	26.1	24.65	23.54	18.67	18.08	24.76	17.89	25.98
23.83	28.5	24.31	25.23	22.89	22.95	24.81	21.69	20.14	19.41	15.19	24.98
28.65	23.1	24.33	27.22	24.29	23.44	22.41	26.17	20.16	28.74	18.61	28.67
25.05	18.09	25.48	27.42	29.03	21.24	25.32	23.22	20.05	27.14	30.94	22.38
24.3	25.75	26.26	18.55	18.6	22.73	26.2	26.95	27.41	28.64	23.77	30.36
13.92	23.26	15.4	26.96	25.86	30.1	24.82	19.49	19.54	13.74	18.25	15.98
29.89	25.88	17.68	24.63	25.01	23.22	23.99	21.6	25.68	25.36	17.79	22.6
20.06	19.42	17.61	29.15	20.51	26.3	27.33	26.71	24.93	25.3	23.56	26.15
24.44	26.93	21.77	20.17	19.46	20.48	21.54	26.36	21.74	25.95	26.59	23.64
21.13	22.54	21.46	22.63	28.67	24.32	28.22	21.73	28.69	27.87	23.16	32.17
23.1	25.04	21.89	25.42	18.45	28.15	27.35	25.8	27.19	26.98	20.81	26.3
13.28	25.27	25.2	19.25	22.95	28.67	20.29	16.59	24.48	23.13	25.54	21.99
21.63	20.26	29.89	19.5	19.81	24.75	13.54	21.26	24.18	25.06	27.44	23.09
22.25	24.61	28.18	22.4	16.9	16.47	28.98	23.84	16.99	12.16	22.51	17.38
27.03	29.03	24.24	27.38	20.42	24.02	20.31	19.99	23.61	29.01	27.72	22.34
22.87	24.57	25.55	28.83	23.33	21.86	26.59	24.17	22.68	29.07	15.13	26.5
20.93	16.85	22.37	21.14	24.5	25.71	29.74	20.31	29.67	27.87	23.19	19.52
22.97	21.86	20.18	25.14	25.14	23.57	17.56	19.58	26.43	31.1	20.7	27.78
24.68	24.35	17.03	21.49	24.12	26.79	18.63	24.67	22.49	16.75	27.94	27.5
15.46	22.48	15.11	22.59	21.76	18.85	20.14	24.62	24.3	29.56	20.67	19.4
21.17	24.48	20.03	27.83	12.61	19.7	23.87	24.94	28.41	24.01	24.62	17.07
28.42	22.41	21.05	17.65	16.57	22.81	26.26	21.42	30.02	21.52	24.44	25.84
24.25	22.53	20.17	22.09	28.9	19.29	26.59	22.03	23.7	21.89	24.6	21.04
21.53	24.35	26.78	15.09	27.13	22.92	25.93	25.22	17.4	18.95	24.51	24.75
19.3	20.41	21.29	26.08	25.98	19.37	23.58	15.27	20.77	26.43	25.28	24.29
20.19	25.31	23.26	26.14	21.68	20.77	26.02	11.94	20.82	23.12	20.64	21.06
32.99	26.54	25.74	23.71	24.8	25.84	27.49	18.73	24.46	29.94	26.84	21.63
25.06	17.01	24.08	23.01	25.35	28.71	24.11	21.96	26.15	20.72	32.7	22.32
20.69	27.73	24.02	22.61	22.87	21.28	26.45	20.31	26.31	28.98	25.17	21.45
26.97	13.1	20.06	20.32	23.3	25.04	26.95	22.39	24.92	17.11	18.82	19.21
21.54	22.44	28.09	22.75	27.38	25.05	27.85	27.96	25.73	24.88	23.76	22.89
15.55	24.15	20.67	19.54	30.5	23.98	24.52	16.16	21.12	15.21	20.16	26.98
16.64	16.74	26.22	27.43	23.19	16.37	16.45	19.97	22.98	22.88	18.81	20.33
20.91	30.99	19.56	25.47	24	25.46	18.02	24.26	19.3	23.1	21.57	27.99
19.24	22.05	22.42	14.53	22.98	26.25	23.49	21.89	23.88	27.74	25.08	26.89
24.84	22.63	19.46	19.61	22.31	27.28	25.24	21.46	20.8	21.39	12.79	18.26
24.43	19.95	23.61	25.01	15.67	29.35	17.19	29.95	26.18			
23.56	27.99	24.74	24.61	17.33	25.89	31.2	28.56	17.94			
23.98	9.72	22.22	23.26	20.67							

Table 3a

Nominal quantity in grams or millilitres	Tolerable Negative Error	
	As a percentage of nominal quantity	g or ml
5 to 50	9	–
50 to 100	–	4.5
100 to 200	4.5	–
200 to 300	–	9
300 to 500	3	–
500 to 1000	–	15
1000 to 10 000	1.5	–
10 000 to 15 000	–	150
Above 15 000	1	–

Table 3b

Non-Destructive Test for Non-Standard Packages: Single Sampling Plan

Number in group	Number in sample	Number of non-standard packages	
		Acceptance criterion	Rejection criterion
100 to 500	50	3	4
501 to 3 200	80	5	6
3 201 and above	125	7	8

Table 3c

Non-Destructive Test for Non-Standard Packages: Double Sampling Plan

Number in group	Samples		Number of non-standard packages		
	Order	Number	Aggregate number	Acceptance criterion	Rejection criterion
100 to 500	1st	30	30	1	3
	2nd	30	60	4	5
501 to 3 200	1st	50	50	2	5
	2nd	50	100	6	7
3 201 and above	1st	80	80	3	7
	2nd	80	160	8	9

Table 3d

Destructive Test for Non-Standard Packages

Number in group	Number in sample	Number of non-standard packages	
		Acceptance criterion	Rejection criterion
Any number above 99	20	1	2

Table 3e

Non-Destructive Test for Average Actual Contents

Number in group	Number in sample	Criteria	
		Acceptance	Rejection
100 to 500	30	$\bar{x} \geq Q_n - 0.503\ s$	$\bar{x} < Q_n - 0.503\ s$
501 and above	50	$\bar{x} \geq Q_n - 0.379\ s$	$\bar{x} < Q_n - 0.379\ s$

Table 3f

Destructive Testing for Average Actual Contents

Number in group	Number in sample	Criteria	
		Acceptance	Rejection
Any number above 99	20	$\bar{x} \geq Q_n - 0.640\ s$	$\bar{x} < Q_n - 0.640\ s$

Index

Bold type indicates main topic.
Standard type indicates topic used in exercise.
Italic type indicates topic used in extension only.